NEW National Cur
Mathematics

M. J. Tipler
K. M. Vickers

Target Book 1

Stanley Thornes (Publishers) Ltd

First published in 1998 by
Stanley Thornes (Publishers) Ltd
Ellenborough House
Wellington Street
CHELTENHAM
GL50 1YW

A catalogue record of this book is available from the British Library

ISBN 0 7487 3546 1

98 99 00 01 02 / 10 9 8 7 6 5 4 3 2 1

The publishers are grateful to the following for permission to
reproduce photographs:

McDonalds: p.127 (right)
Martyn F Chillmaid: pp.68 (left and right), 211, 223
Pizza Hut: p.127 (left)

Typeset and Illustrated by Hardlines, Charlbury, Oxford
Printed and bound in Spain by Mateu Cromo

Contents

Preface

Welcome to Target Book 1. We know you will enjoy working with it.

You can learn maths by doing it.

In this book, there are lots of clear examples to show you what to do and then lots of ways to practise.

This book is full of interesting and exciting activities to help you understand and enjoy maths.

Exercises – these are graded so the easy ones come first.

Investigations – these have things for you to discover.

Tasks – these have things for you to do.

Games – these are an interesting way for you to practise your skills.

Puzzles – try and solve these.

Each chapter has Homework/Reviews that your teacher may give you for homework or in class. They are for you to practise what you have learnt in the last few pages.

At the end of each chapter there is a Chapter Review. This is like a chapter test to see what you have remembered. Your teacher may give it to you at the end of the chapter or at some other time during the year.

Maths is all around you. It will be part of whatever you choose to do when you leave school. Target Books 1–5 will give you a good maths education up to GCSE.

Best wishes for an enjoyable and successful year in maths.

M J Tipler
K M Vickers

1 Numbers

Going places...

Cars, trains and buses all have numbers. Why?

Why might these have numbers?

- taxis
- ships
- lorries
- racehorses
- yachts
- planes
- birds
- people

Place value

Remember . . .

45 means 4 tens and 5 ones.

54 means 5 tens and 4 ones.

Exercise 1

Write down what goes in the boxes.
The first one is done.

1. 29 means | 2 tens | and | 9 ones |

2. 36 means | 3 | and | 6 |

3. 84 means | 8 | and | 4 |

4. 12 means | 1 | and | 2 |

5. 60 means | 6 | and | 0 |

6. 37 means [   ] and [   ]

7. 71 means [   ] and [   ]

8. 18 means [   ] and [   ]

9. 29 means [   ] and [   ]

10. 40 means [   ] and [   ]

Exercise 2   How many tens are in these?

1. 14	2. 54	3. 37	4. 82
5. 61	6. 94	7. 19	8. 30

Exercise 3   How many ones are in these?

1. 52	2. 11	3. 74	4. 98
5. 23	6. 75	7. 58	8. 50

37 can be shown as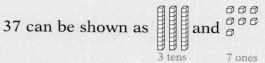

99 can be shown as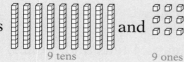

What happens to 99 if we add another one?

324 can be shown as

239 can be shown as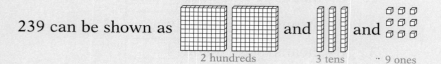

Example   856 means 8 hundreds and 5 tens and 6 ones.

Exercise 4   Write down what goes in the boxes.

The first one is done.

1. 724 means | 7 hundreds | and | 2 tens | and | 4 ones |

2. 386 means [   ] and [   ] and [   ]

3. 239 means [   ] and [   ] and [   ]

4. 142 means [   ] and [   ] and [   ]

5. 989 means [   ] and [   ] and [   ]

6. 465 means [   ] and [   ] and [   ]

7. 751 means [   ] and [   ] and [   ]

Exercise 5   Write these as numbers.

1. 4 hundreds and 5 tens and 3 ones

2. 7 hundreds and 6 tens and 2 ones

3. 6 hundreds and 3 tens and 9 ones

4. 8 hundreds and 7 tens and 1 one

5. 1 hundred and 4 tens and 8 ones

6. 3 hundreds and 9 tens and 6 ones

7. 2 hundreds and 1 ten and 1 one

8. 9 hundreds and 8 tens and 4 ones

Exercise 6   How many hundreds are in these?

1. 500	2. 600	3. 415	4. 735
5. 642	6. 103	7. 507	8. 870
9. 950	10. 235	11. 361	

Exercise 7   How many tens are in these?

1. 623	2. 584	3. 670	4. 820
5. 948	6. 389	7. 243	8. 649
9. 104	10. 202	11. 705	

Examples 9 hundreds is written as 900.

5 hundreds and 4 tens is written as 540.

8 hundreds and 3 ones is written as 803.

Exercise 8 Write these as numbers.

1. 6 hundreds
2. 8 hundreds
3. 4 hundreds and 2 tens
4. 9 hundreds and 4 tens
5. 7 hundreds and 5 tens
6. 5 hundreds and 3 ones
7. 1 hundred and 7 ones
8. 2 hundreds and 4 ones
9. 7 hundreds and 4 tens
10. 3 hundreds and 6 tens

Exercise 9 **What kind of bars won't keep a burglar in jail?**

| 340 | 500 | 58 | 340 | 58 | 564 | A 804 | 405 | E 70 |

| 511 | A 804 | 931 | 780 |

Use a copy of this box.

Find the number, in the box, that matches the words below.

Write the letter that is beside the words on the line above the number.

The first two have been done for you.

E 7 tens
H 5 hundreds
O 5 tens and 8 ones
S 7 hundreds and 8 tens
R 9 hundreds and 3 tens
   and 1 one

A 8 hundreds and 4 ones
T 4 hundreds and 5 ones
C 3 hundreds and 4 tens
B 5 hundreds and 1 ten
   and 1 one
L 5 hundreds and 6 tens
   and 4 ones

The **place** of a number tells you its **value**.

This chart shows place value for 324.

The 3 means 3 hundreds.

The 2 means 2 tens.

The 4 means 4 ones.

Hundreds	Tens	Ones
3	2	4

Exercise 10

Use a copy of this place value chart.

Fill it in.

The first one is done.

	Hundreds	Tens	Ones
406	4	0	6
572			
381			
604			
935			
760			
610			

Example   The place value of 8 in the number 843 is 8 hundreds.

The place value of 5 in the number 452 is 5 tens.

Exercise 11   **A**   What is the place value of the 7?

1.
357

2.
Watton A705

3.
670

B   What is the place value of the 6?

1.
634

2.
546

3. 306

C   What is the place value of the 3?

1.
934

2.
223

3.
430

Homework/Review 1

A Write down what goes in the boxes.

The first one is done.

1. 752 means | 7 hundreds | and | 5 tens | and | 2 ones |
2. 812 means [　　] and [　　] and [　　]
3. 640 means [　　] and [　　] and [　　]
4. 307 means [　　] and [　　] and [　　]

B How many hundreds are in these?

  1. 681   2. 508   3. 340   4. 724

C **Why did the clock get put in jail?**

                    U
605   72   930   430   50   520   72   43   60

              U   L
520   60   802   50   930   934   60   600   72   620   821   72

Use a copy of this box.
Find the number, in the box, that matches the words below.
Write the letter that is beside the words on the line above
the number.

The first two have been done for you.

U	5 tens		**L**	6 hundreds and 2 tens
W	6 hundreds		**C**	9 hundreds and 3 tens
A	4 hundreds and 3 tens		**V**	8 hundreds and 2 tens
E	7 tens and 2 ones			and 1 one
K	9 hundreds and 3 tens		**R**	8 hundreds and 2 ones
	and 4 ones		**S**	5 hundreds and 2 tens
I	4 tens and 3 ones		**B**	6 hundreds and 5 ones
T	6 tens			

D What is the place value of the 5?

1.

2.

3.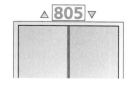

Reading and writing numbers

Examples   86 is written as eighty six.

Forty nine is written as 49.

Exercise 12   **A**   Write these in words.

1. 57   2. 21   3. 13   4. 34
5. 85   6. 79   7. 92   8. 54
9. 68   10. 46   11. 60   12. 99

B   Write these in numbers.

1. Twelve

2. Nineteen

3. Thirty seven

4. Fifty two

5. Ninety six
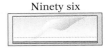

6. Forty three
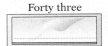

7. Seventy one
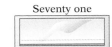

8. Eighty five
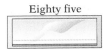

Example   On cheques:

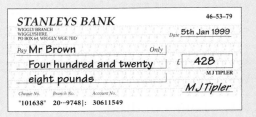

STANLEYS BANK   46–53–79
WIGGLY BRANCH
WIGGLYSHIRE
PO BOX 64, WIGGLY, WGE 7BD   *Date* 5th Jan 1999
Pay **Mr Brown**   *Only*
Four hundred and twenty   £   428
eight pounds   M J TIPLER
Cheque No.   *Branch No.*   *Account No.*   *MJTipler*
"101638"   20···9748|:   30611549

Exercise 13   **A**   Write these in words.

1. £600   2. £700   3. £582   4. £829
5. £431   6. £989   7. £365   8. £211
9. £718   10. £104   11. £560   12. £720
13. £809   14. £714   15. £301   16. £899

B These dogs won a prize in a show.

486 Ben 304 Tip 220 Zak 681 Sam 324 Kate

511 Pip 700 Biff 104 Sandy 699 Rita 325 Tina

Use a copy of this table.

Fill it in.

The first one is done.

Name of dog	Number in words
Ben	four hundred and eighty six
Tip	
Zak	
Sam	
Kate	
Pip	
Biff	
Sandy	
Rita	
Tina	

Exercise 14

Write in numbers.

1. Four hundred
2. Three hundred and twenty
3. Six hundred and eighty four
4. Nine hundred and thirty four
5. Three hundred and five
6. One hundred and twenty eight
7. Seven hundred and sixty
8. Eight hundred and ninety nine
9. Four hundred and twelve
10. Six hundred and nineteen
11. Five hundred and nine
12. One hundred and eleven

Exercise 15   Menna showed her house number in 4 different ways.

Use a copy of these.

Fill them in.

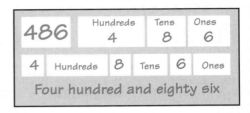

Adam's house

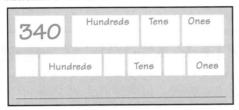

Ben's house

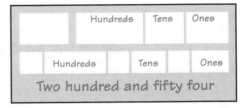

Anna's house

Sara's house

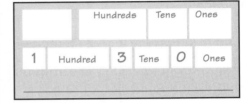

Homework/Review 2

A Write these in words.

| 1. | 68 | 2. | 47 | 3. | 321 | 4. | 672 |
| 5. | 804 | 6. | 320 | 7. | 903 | | |

B Write these as numbers.

1. Forty two
2. Six hundred and thirty three
3. Five hundred and seventy
4. Eight hundred and four
5. Seven hundred and one

C Use a copy of this and fill it in.

Number in words	Number
six hundred and forty two	
	304
seven hundred and five	
	820
	999

Puzzle

How many different numbers can you make using these?

4   6   3

Examples 4   63   66   634   336

◀◀ CHAPTER REVIEW ◀◀

◀◀
Exercise 4
on page 3

A Write down what goes in the boxes.

The first one is done.

1. 964 means | 9 hundreds | and | 6 tens | and | 4 ones |

2. 231 means [   ] and [   ] and [   ]

3. 785 means [   ] and [   ] and [   ]

◀◀
Exercise 5
on page 3

B Write these as numbers.

1. 7 hundreds and 4 tens and 5 ones

2. 6 hundreds and 8 tens and 2 ones

◀◀
Exercise 6
on page 3

C How many hundreds are in these?

1. 516   2. 271   3. 384   4. 105

◀◀
Exercise 8
on page 4

D Write these as numbers.

1. 5 hundreds   2. 4 hundreds and 3 tens
3. 8 hundreds and 2 ones   4. 7 hundreds and 4 ones

◀◀
Exercise 10
on page 5

E Use a copy of this.

Fill it in.

	Hundreds	Tens	Ones
474	4	7	4
681			
720			
304			
500			

Exercise 11
on page 5

F What is the value of the 2?

1.

2.

3.

Exercise 13
on page 7

G Write these in words.

1. £724   2. £830   3. £402   4. £913

Exercise 14
on page 8

H This is Sam's front door.

What numbers go on these doors?

1.

2.

3.

2 Putting Numbers in Order

Winning..

In golf, the person with the lowest number wins.

How do we decide who wins in these?

- high jump
- swimming
- weight lifting
- football
- boxing
- computer games

Biggest and smallest

54 has more tens than 46.

54 is bigger than 46.

68 has the same number of tens as 63.

So we look at the ones.

8 is bigger than 3.

So 68 is bigger than 63.

Exercise 1   **A**   Which is bigger?

1. 20 or 30
2. 56 or 34
3. 68 or 71
4. 79 or 71
5. 83 or 89
6. 57 or 71
7. 55 or 52
8. 64 or 69

B Which is smaller?

1. 40 or 50   2. 18 or 21   3. 78 or 81
4. 28 or 21   5. 63 or 67   6. 57 or 82
7. 96 or 49   8. 79 or 71

Example

84 is the biggest number.

53 is the smallest number.

Exercise 2   **A** Which is the biggest number?

1. 57, 84, 61, 78, 92   2. 34, 53, 29, 19, 49
3. 78, 92, 34, 73, 95   4. 27, 29, 21, 35, 31
5. 58, 42, 55, 49, 50   6. 92, 87, 83, 91, 79, 81

B Which is the smallest number?

1. 52, 65, 78, 31, 42   2. 91, 78, 63, 42, 94
3. 41, 54, 33, 29, 38   4. 56, 42, 43, 50, 40
5. 62, 81, 63, 84, 61, 60   6. 93, 90, 89, 81, 94, 82

583 has more hundreds than 421.
So 583 is bigger than 421.
Why do we look at the hundreds first?

687 and 639 have the same number of hundreds.
So we look at the tens.
687 has more tens than 639.
687 is bigger than 639.

Exercise 3   **A** Which is bigger?

1. 300 or 600   2. 650 or 720   3. 361 or 427
4. 472 or 801   5. 900 or 301   6. 637 or 673
7. 298 or 289   8. 442 or 453   9. 862 or 867
10. 777 or 775   11. 532 or 723   12. 781 or 794

B Which is smaller?

1. 500 or 200	2. 890 or 560	3. 532 or 294
4. 800 or 798	5. 342 or 324	6. 432 or 441
7. 734 or 771	8. 753 or 751	

Exercise 4

Use of copy of this.

83	95	101	168	186	197	204	211	225	237	239	243	259
268	274	283	290	309	317	324	333	351	364	379	384	396
419	421	434	443	478	487	500	515	525	534	552	568	586
604	613	631	639	640	652	659	683	705	724	738	741	759
795	812	825	852	859	874	903	926	962	968	986	990	999

Choose the biggest number from each list.

Shade the box it is in.

The first two are done.

1. 478, 613, 604	2. 309, 903, 874	3. 568, 586, 552
4. 290, 317, 309	5. 83, 101, 95	6. 239, 237, 243
7. 259, 239, 237	8. 225, 239, 237	9. 61, 83, 79
10. 525, 534, 552	11. 204, 197, 101	12. 926, 986, 968
13. 874, 825, 795	14. 421, 419, 396	15. 990, 759, 999
16. 812, 795, 639	17. 101, 211, 186	18. 396, 478, 487
19. 379, 364, 351	20. 168, 197, 186	21. 487, 500, 515
22. 990, 986, 968	23. 168, 268, 259	24. 396, 568, 552
25. 283, 274, 259	26. 604, 652, 639	27. 500, 487, 478
28. 705, 741, 759	29. 243, 274, 268	30. 874, 903, 926

Exercise 5

1. Use 3 of these numbers to make the biggest number you can.

2. Use 3 of these numbers to make the smallest number you can.

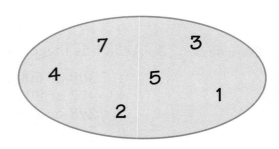

Exercise 6   These are number cards.

Pam won these.

She made the number
436 with her cards.

1.   What is a smaller number Pam could make?

2.   What is the biggest number Pam could make?

Game for a group: BIGGEST NUMBER

You will need   a copy of this chart for each player

Hundreds	Tens	Ones

To play
- Pick a leader.
- The leader calls out 3 numbers one by one.
  The numbers called must be less than 10.
- As each number is called, the other players put it in one of the boxes.
- The players who make the biggest number win 1 point.

Example   If the numbers called are 6, 7 and 3, these charts can be made.

Hundreds	Tens	Ones
3	6	7

Hundreds	Tens	Ones
3	7	6

Hundreds	Tens	Ones
7	6	3

Hundreds	Tens	Ones
6	7	3

Hundreds	Tens	Ones
6	3	7

Hundreds	Tens	Ones
7	3	6

The players who made 763 get 1 point.

- The first to get 5 points is the new leader.

Homework/Review 1

A   Which is bigger?

    1.   87 or 91   **2.**   68 or 63   **3.**   77 or 69

    4.   386 or 354   **5.**   792 or 799

B   Which is smaller?

    1.   64 or 82   **2.**   655 or 565   **3.**   524 or 529

    4.   783 or 387   **5.**   983 or 938

C   **What is the best thing to do if a bull charges you?**

	A					
516	572	479		463	614	533

Use a copy of the box.
Pick the biggest number in each row.
Fill in the box.
The first one is done.

A   327, 533, 463, 479, 572

I   327, 479, 533, 614, 463

Y   387, 463, 327, 479, 459

M   459, 533, 516, 463, 479

H   132, 459, 463, 387, 327

P   516, 479, 459, 132, 327

D

0 1 2 3 4 5 6 7 8 9

These are number cards.

Ned picked 3 of them.
He made the number 587
with his cards.

    1.   What is a smaller number Ned could make?

    2.   What is the biggest number Ned can make?

Putting numbers in order

To put numbers **in order** from biggest to smallest

- pick the biggest number
- pick the next biggest number
- keep picking the biggest number out of the numbers left.

Example

The biggest is 82. The next biggest is 78.

The next is 61. The last is 53.

In order from biggest to smallest these are 82, 78, 61, 53.

Exercise 7   **A**   Put these in order from biggest to smallest.

1. 78, 63, 51, 89, 92, 42
2. 33, 29, 19, 56, 42, 65
3. 81, 63, 54, 79, 94, 42
4. 83, 96, 41, 53, 64, 72
5. 39, 37, 42, 31, 44, 46
6. 78, 63, 75, 64, 72, 65

B   Put these in order from biggest to smallest.

1. 532, 376, 421, 783, 264
2. 384, 176, 423, 894, 932
3. 652, 341, 427, 614, 734
4. 552, 840, 564, 837, 652
5. 732, 745, 768, 752, 787
6. 963, 952, 904, 994, 937

To put numbers **in order** from smallest to biggest

- pick the smallest number
- keep picking the smallest number from the numbers left.

Example   387, 592, 261, 432

The smallest is 261. The next smallest is 387.

The next is 432. The last is 592.

In order from smallest to biggest these are 261, 387, 432, 592.

Exercise 8   Put these in order from smallest to biggest.

1. 89, 81, 79, 77, 73, 84
2. 64, 63, 60, 59, 51, 72
3. 324, 468, 572, 151, 752
4. 891, 864, 736, 852, 741
5. 584, 622, 601, 619, 596
6. 729, 736, 752, 794, 711
7. 432, 444, 457, 449, 486
8. 234, 227, 239, 229, 230

Exercise 9   These are number cards.

Make as many different numbers as you can using all 3 cards.

Put your numbers in order from biggest to smallest.

Game for a class or group: FIVE UP

You will need   a copy of this for each player

To play
- Choose a leader. This could be your teacher.
- The leader calls out 5 numbers between 100 and 999.
- As each number is called, players write it in one of the boxes so that the numbers are in order.
- If a number cannot be put in order then it is not written down.
- The winner is the player with the most numbers written down.

Example   This is what Ruth wrote.

The leader called 386.

			386	

The leader called 279.

			386	279

The leader called 846.

846			386	279

The leader called 904.
Ruth could not write this down.

846			386	279

The leader called 345.
Ruth could not write this down.

846			386	279

Ruth got 3 numbers written down in order.

We often need to put numbers in order
to find the answer to a question.

Example Who won the high jump?
Who got second?

High jump	
Ben	112 cm
Vijay	115 cm
Ray	111 cm

Answer 115 is the biggest number. Vijay won the high jump.

112 is the next biggest number. Ben got second.

Exercise 10 **A** Who won the high jump? Who got second?

1.

High jump	
Liz	111 cm
Cathy	109 cm
Elen	114 cm

2.

High jump	
Owen	116 cm
David	112 cm
Rishi	117 cm

B Who is the tallest? Who is the second tallest?

1.

Name	Height
Tim	148 cm
Ben	142 cm
Sam	151 cm
Tom	143 cm
Harry	139 cm
Farid	149 cm

2.

Name	Height
Sara	152 cm
Ali	155 cm
Tandy	148 cm
Lisa	150 cm
Misa	149 cm
Anna	156 cm

C Who got the most points? Who was next?

1.

Name	Points
Jane	386
Mike	372
Alex	396
Clare	382
Emma	387

2.

Name	Points
Dean	472
Akira	479
Tom	483
Steve	477
Peter	461

Homework/Review 2

A Put these in order from biggest to smallest.

    1. 72, 81, 96, 54, 63, 41   **2.** 19, 47, 98, 52, 86, 32

    3. 64, 72, 89, 74, 63, 82   **4.** 29, 37, 24, 38, 41, 33

    5. 500, 279, 368, 427, 143   **6.** 186, 173, 784, 796, 635

B Put these in order from smallest to biggest.

    1. 83, 74, 65, 15, 94, 21   **2.** 25, 98, 11, 36, 52, 49

    3. 39, 37, 31, 29, 38, 27   **4.** 187, 182, 186, 193, 121

    5. 583, 524, 579, 589, 541   **6.** 493, 486, 404, 417, 490

C

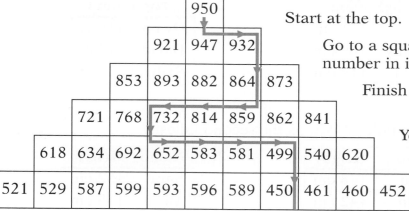

Use a copy of this.

Start at the top.

Go to a square that has a *smaller* number in it.

Finish at the bottom.

You may go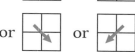

Find as many ways as you can.

One is done for you.

D Who is the tallest? Who is the second tallest?

1.

Name	Height
Jon	153 cm
Tim	152 cm
Ray	150 cm
Ben	154 cm
Carl	149 cm
David	151 cm

2.

Name	Height
Amy	160 cm
Ann	158 cm
Cath	162 cm
Emma	159 cm
Gwen	163 cm
Jean	159 cm

D
1. Sudi counted 4 black kittens, 3 white kittens and 1 grey kitten.
   How many kittens is this?

2. Jo counted 3 tan puppies, 2 black puppies and 2 brown puppies.
   How many puppies is this?

3. Karl counted 3 blue birds, 4 green birds and 2 grey birds.
   How many birds is this?

5	2	2
0	3	6
4	4	1

This is called a **magic square**.

We get the same answer no matter which way we add.

Examples

5	2	2
0	3	6
4	4	1

5 + 2 + 2 = 9

5	2	2
0	3	6
4	4	1

5 + 0 + 4 = 9

5	2	2
0	3	6
4	4	1

2 + 3 + 4 = 9

Exercise 3

Use a copy of these magic squares. Fill them in.

1.
3	2	1
	2	

2.
4		
0	3	
5		

3.
3		
		3
5		3

Game for 2 players: MAKE TEN

You will need 3 green counters

3 red counters

To play
- Players take turns to put a counter on a number **or** move one of their counters to another number.
- You cannot have 2 counters on the same number.
- Try to make 10 with your 3 counters.
- The winner is the first person to do this.

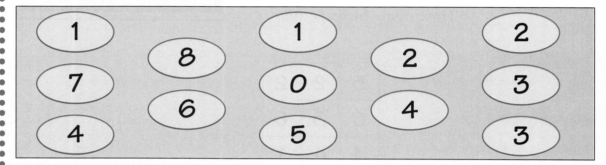

Adding to 20

Learn the **addition facts** on this table.

+	0	1	2	3	4	5	6	7	8	9	10	11	12	13	14	15	16	17	18	19	20
0	0	1	2	3	4	5	6	7	8	9	10	11	12	13	14	15	16	17	18	19	20
1	1	2	3	4	5	6	7	8	9	10	11	12	13	14	15	16	17	18	19	20	
2	2	3	4	5	6	7	8	9	10	11	12	13	14	15	16	17	18	19	20		
3	3	4	5	6	7	8	9	10	11	12	13	14	15	16	17	18	19	20			
4	4	5	6	7	8	9	10	11	12	13	14	15	16	17	18	19	20				
5	5	6	7	8	9	10	11	12	13	14	15	16	17	18	19	20					
6	6	7	8	9	10	11	12	13	14	15	16	17	18	19	20						
7	7	8	9	10	11	12	13	14	15	16	17	18	19	20							
8	8	9	10	11	12	13	14	15	16	17	18	19	20								
9	9	10	11	12	13	14	15	16	17	18	19	20									
10	10	11	12	13	14	15	16	17	18	19	20										

Ways to help you remember the additions

● Learn the doubles.

$6 + 6 = 12$
$7 + 7 = 14$
$8 + 8 = 16$
$9 + 9 = 18$
$10 + 10 = 20$

● Learn the pattern when we add a number to 10.

$10 + 1 = 11$
$10 + 2 = 12$
$10 + 3 = 13$
$10 + 4 = 14$
$10 + 5 = 15$

What are the answers to these?

$10 + 7$
$10 + 8$
$10 + 9$
$10 + 10$

● Use your 'addition facts to 10' to help.

$2 + 3 = 5$	$4 + 5 = 9$	$3 + 6 = 9$	$4 + 3 = 7$
$12 + 3 = 15$	$14 + 5 = 19$	$13 + 6 = 19$	$4 + 13 = 17$

What are the answers to these?

$15 + 3$
$17 + 2$
$14 + 6$
$12 + 7$

● Use the facts you know well.

$7 + 7 = 14$
$7 + 6 = 13$ 6 is one less than 7. The answer is one less than 14.

$10 + 6 = 16$
$9 + 6 = 15$ 9 is one less than 10. The answer is one less than 16.

What are the answers to these?

$9 + 7$
$6 + 5$
$9 + 8$

Exercise 4   **A**   Find the answers to these.

1. 10 + 3	2. 10 + 5	3. 7 + 7
4. 4 + 10	5. 6 + 6	6. 3 + 10
7. 8 + 8	8. 7 + 6	9. 9 + 9
10. 8 + 7	11. 5 + 9	12. 4 + 10
13. 9 + 3	14. 6 + 7	15. 7 + 8
16. 9 + 6	17. 9 + 8	18. 5 + 8
19. 6 + 8	20. 12 + 2	21. 11 + 4

22.   13
    + 5
	23. 14
	    + 6
		24. 12
		    + 8

B   What number goes in the box?

1. 8 + ☐ = 12	2. 9 + ☐ = 12	3. 6 + ☐ = 15
4. 5 + ☐ = 16	5. 7 + ☐ = 15	6. 8 + ☐ = 17
7. 9 + ☐ = 15	8. 8 + ☐ = 20	9. 7 + ☐ = 13

Exercise 5   **A**   Use a copy of these.
                Fill in the missing numbers.

1.

+	7	4	5
8	15	12	
10	17		
9			

2.

+	14	15	13
4			
3			
5			

3.

+	8	7	6
6			
12			
11			

B   Use a copy of this.
      Find numbers to go in the green squares.
      Try to find more than one way.

+		
	17	15
	14	

Exercise 6   Four of these additions are *not* true.
                Write down the letters which are beside these.
                Make a word from these letters.

K	7 + 7 = 16		N	4 + 16 = 20		P	8 + 8 = 16
C	8 + 7 = 15		F	5 + 11 = 16		L	8 + 7 = 15
E	10 + 6 = 17		T	12 + 7 = 19		B	7 + 0 = 7
Y	9 + 4 = 13		S	14 + 6 = 20		O	5 + 8 = 13
D	8 + 3 = 11		M	17 + 2 = 20		A	7 + 9 = 15

Investigation

Copy these. Write down the answers.

4 + 3 =	7 + 6 =	8 + 9 =	8 + 7 =
3 + 4 =	6 + 7 =	9 + 8 =	7 + 8 =
5 + 14 =	13 + 6 =	15 + 4 =	12 + 6 =
14 + 5 =	6 + 13 =	4 + 15 =	6 + 12 =

Copy this sentence. Fill in the gap with *can* or *cannot*.

We _____ add in any order.

Exercise 7   Find two numbers from the ring that add to less than 20. Find as many ways as you can. One way is 8 + 7 = 15

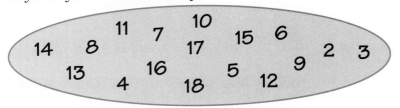

Example   Ross saved £4 one week and £11 the next.
How much had he saved in two weeks?

Answer   4 + 11 = 15.
Ross had saved £15.

Exercise 8   **A**   Claire was on her way to school.

1. She counted 12 people on the bus.
    Then 5 more got on.
    How many were on the bus then?

2. She counted 13 people on the train.
    Then 6 more got on.
    How many were on the train then?

3. She counted 11 people at the school gate.
    Then 7 more came.
    How many were at the school gate then?

B Claire wrote down how many minutes she wrote for in class.

In Maths I wrote for 11 + 6 minutes.	In French I wrote for 14 + 5 minutes.	In Science I wrote for 9 + 8 minutes.

How long did she write for altogether in these?

1. Maths   **2.** French   **3.** Science

C Claire's class had a test.

It had two parts.

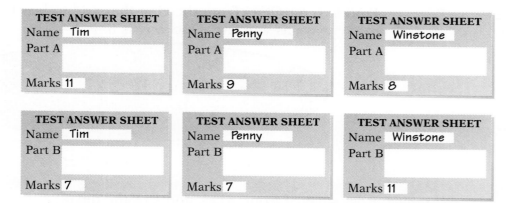

TEST ANSWER SHEET Name Tim Part A Marks 11	**TEST ANSWER SHEET** Name Penny Part A Marks 9	**TEST ANSWER SHEET** Name Winstone Part A Marks 8
TEST ANSWER SHEET Name Tim Part B Marks 7	**TEST ANSWER SHEET** Name Penny Part B Marks 7	**TEST ANSWER SHEET** Name Winstone Part B Marks 11

How many marks altogether did these get?

1. Tim   **2.** Penny   **3.** Winstone

D Claire wrote these about her family.

> Rasha is 7 years older than Julie. Julie is 12.
>
> Sarah is 5 years older than John. John is 13.
>
> Kim is 9 years older than Jake. Jake is 11.

1. How old is Rasha?

2. How old is Sarah?

3. How old is Kim?

Homework/Review 1

A Write down the answers to these.

1. 10 + 4
2. 10 + 7
3. 10 + 8
4. 7 + 6
5. 8 + 7
6. 9 + 8
7. 8 + 6
8. 5 + 9
9. 4 + 11
10. 3 + 12
11. 11 + 6
12. 13 + 5
13. 11
    + 9
14. 12
    + 7
15. 14
    + 5

B James played a game with darts.
He threw two darts and added the numbers.
What did he get in these games?

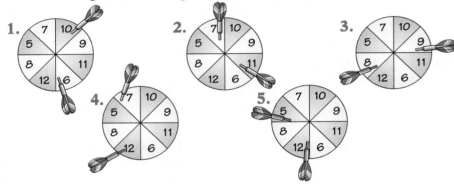

C What is this a picture of?
Use a copy of the box below.

To find the answer:
Do each addition. Find the answer in the box below.
Write the letter beside the addition on top of its answer.
The first two have been done for you.

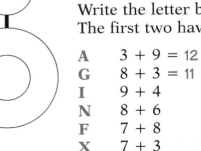

A   3 + 9 = 12
G   8 + 3 = 11
I   9 + 4
N   8 + 6
F   7 + 8
X   7 + 3
C   14 + 6
Y   11 + 6
E   12 + 6
R   11 + 8
M   7 + 9

A						A	
12	16	18	10	13	20	12	14

					G	A	
15	19	17	13	14	11	12	14

	G	G
18	11	11

More adding

We can add numbers in any order.

When we add more than two numbers, we add the two numbers that are easiest to add **first**.

$4 + 5 + 6 = 10 + 5$ It is easiest to add $4 + 6$ to get 10.

Easiest to add $= 15$

Which two numbers are easiest to add first in these?

$8 + 7 + 2$	$9 + 6 + 4$	$8 + 7 + 3$
$1 + 8 + 9$	$7 + 6 + 2$	$9 + 5 + 4$
$12 + 3 + 5$	$14 + 3 + 3$	

Exercise 9

A Add these.

1. $5 + 2 + 1$	2. $8 + 4 + 2$	3. $7 + 6 + 4$
4. $9 + 5 + 1$	5. $11 + 3 + 2$	6. $5 + 4 + 3$
7. $6 + 2 + 9$	8. $8 + 7 + 4$	9. $6 + 8 + 5$
10. $7 + 5 + 4$	11. $6 + 7 + 5$	12. $8 + 9 + 2$
13. $4 + 4 + 8$	14. $5 + 9 + 6$	15. $7 + 0 + 9$

16.
$$\begin{array}{r} 13 \\ 3 \\ + 3 \\ \hline \end{array}$$
17.
$$\begin{array}{r} 11 \\ 5 \\ + 3 \\ \hline \end{array}$$
18.
$$\begin{array}{r} 12 \\ 4 \\ + 2 \\ \hline \end{array}$$

19.
$$\begin{array}{r} 15 \\ 1 \\ + 4 \\ \hline \end{array}$$
20.
$$\begin{array}{r} 12 \\ 4 \\ + 3 \\ \hline \end{array}$$
21.
$$\begin{array}{r} 11 \\ 3 \\ + 4 \\ \hline \end{array}$$

22.
$$\begin{array}{r} 7 \\ 8 \\ + 5 \\ \hline \end{array}$$
23.
$$\begin{array}{r} 12 \\ 5 \\ + 3 \\ \hline \end{array}$$

B What number goes in the box?

1. $7+3+\square=16$	2. $8+4+\square=14$	3. $10+3+\square=16$
4. $9+6+\square=17$	5. $5+6+\square=14$	6. $9+7+\square=18$
7. $7+5+\square=16$	8. $11+4+\square=19$	9. $\square+3+3=14$
10. $\square+4+9=16$	11. $\square+5+4=15$	12. $\square+4+6=13$
13. $5+\square+3=14$	14. $9+\square+5=18$	15. $6+\square+7=17$
16. $11+\square+4=19$	17. $12+\square+3=17$	18. $13+\square+0=15$

Exercise 10   **A** Use of copy of these.
Each row of 3 circles must add to the same number.
Fill in the empty circles.

1. 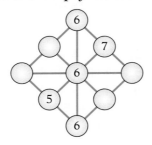   2.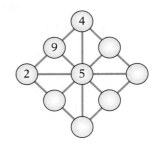

B These are magic squares.
Use a copy of them.
Fill in the missing numbers.

1.

8	3	4
6		

2.

10		
1		11
7		

3.

8		3
	5	
		2

Exercise 11   Choose 3 numbers from the ring which add to 20.
Do this in as many ways as you can.
One way is 13 + 4 + 3 = 20.

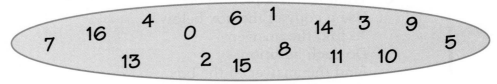

. . . .

Puzzle

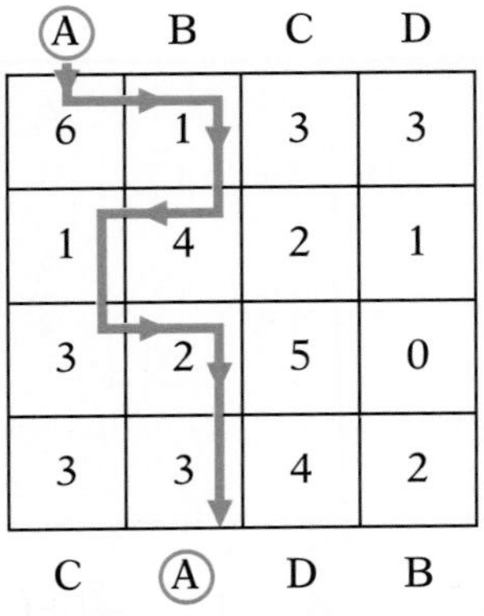

	B	C	D
6	1	3	3
1	4	2	1
3	2	5	0
3	3	4	2

(Ⓐ at top left, C Ⓐ D B at bottom)

Use a copy of this.
Start at a letter at the top. Finish at the same letter at the bottom. Add the numbers in the squares as you go.
They must add to 20.

You may go  or 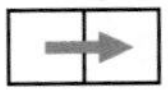 or

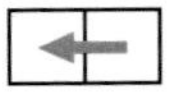

but **not**  or ... or ... or ... or ...

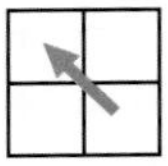

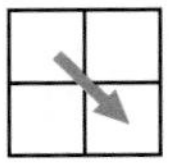

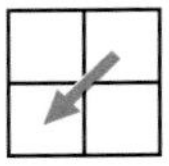

A is done for you. **A** is 6 + 1 + 4 + 1 + 3 + 2 + 3.

Homework/Review 2

A   Add these.

1. 6 + 4 + 2   2. 7 + 4 + 3   3. 8 + 4 + 2
4. 5 + 6 + 4   5. 7 + 2 + 8   6. 5 + 6 + 5
7. 8 + 3 + 8   8. 4 + 3 + 9   9. 8 + 7 + 4
10. 6 + 9 + 5   11. 11 + 5 + 2   12. 9 + 6 + 5
13.   4   14.   13   15.   6
       14   4   11
      + 2   + 0   + 3

B   These are magic squares.
Use a copy of them.
Fill in the missing numbers.

1.
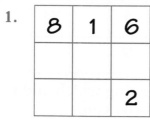

2.
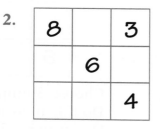

C   What is this a picture of?
Use a copy of the box below.
To find the answer:
Do each addition.
Find the answer in the box.
Write the letter that is beside the addition on top of its answer.
The first one has been done for you.

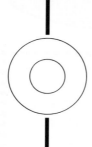

A   3 + 4 + 2 = 9
G   6 + 9 + 3
I   8 + 7 + 1
C   9 + 6 + 2
N   3 + 0 + 11
E   3 + 6 + 4
M   4 + 5 + 2
X   8 + 5 + 7
R   8 + 4 + 0
K   7 + 5 + 3
B   9 + 7 + 3
D   0 + 3 + 7

A							A	
9		11	13	20	16	17	9	14

						A
12	16	10	16	14	18	9

19	16	15	13

Game for a group: ADDITION BINGO

You will need   9 counters for each player
a card like this for
each player

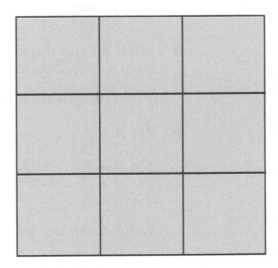

To play • Write a different
number in each
square of your card
(the numbers should
be between 0 and 20).

• Choose a leader.

• The leader calls out an
addition that has an
answer between 0 and 20.

Examples   4 + 8   3 + 12   8 + 11   7 + 9   8 + 0

• If the answer is on your card, cover it with a counter.

• The first person to have all the numbers covered is the winner.
This person is the new leader.

Investigation

● Copy these.
Write down the answers.

3 + 3 =	3 + 5 =	3 + 7 =	3 + 9 =
5 + 7 =	5 + 9 =	5 + 11 =	9 + 1 =
9 + 11 =	11 + 3 =	13 + 3 =	

Look at the numbers you added.
Are they all odd or all even?
Look at the answers.
Copy this sentence. Fill in the gap.

When we add two odd numbers we get an _____ number.

● Copy these. Write down the answers.

$2 + 2 =$ $2 + 4 =$ $4 + 6 =$ $8 + 6 =$

Write a sentence about adding two even numbers.

● What do you think will happen when you add an odd and an even number? Copy and finish this sentence.

When we add an odd and an even number _____

● $0 + 1 = 1$
$1 + 2 = 3$
$2 + 3 = 5$
$3 + 4 = 7$
$9 + 5 = 9$

Write down the next 5 lines of this pattern.

Try to write down a pattern which makes even numbers.

• •

◀◀ CHAPTER REVIEW ◀◀

• •

◀◀

Exercise 1
on page 25

A Find the answers to these.

1. $1 + 7$	2. $5 + 5$	3. $4 + 0$
4. $3 + 4$	5. $6 + 2$	6. $5 + 3$
7. $4 + 5$	8. $6 + 4$	9. $7 + 3$
10. $3 + 2 + 1$	11. $8 + 1 + 1$	12. $4 + 0 + 5$
13. $2 + 3 + 4$	14. $6 + 2 + 1$	15. $3 + 5 + 2$

◀◀

Exercise 4
on page 30

B Find the answers to these.

1. $6 + 5$	2. $8 + 3$	3. $9 + 4$
4. $8 + 5$	5. $9 + 6$	6. $7 + 6$
7. $9 + 7$	8. $4 + 9$	9. $11 + 5$
10. $\begin{array}{r} 12 \\ + 6 \\ \hline \end{array}$	11. $\begin{array}{r} 14 \\ + 5 \\ \hline \end{array}$	12. $\begin{array}{r} 12 \\ + 8 \\ \hline \end{array}$

◀◀

Exercise 5
on page 30

C Use a copy of this.
Fill in the missing numbers.

+	9	8	7
5			
9			
4			

◀◀
Exercise 7
on page 31

D Pat plays a game at a fair. She throws 2 balls. She wins if the numbers on the baskets add to 15.

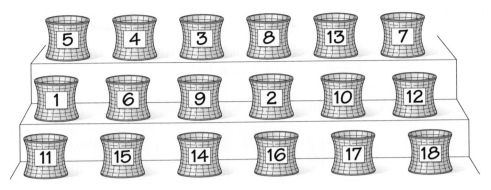

Which two baskets could Pat's balls go in to make 15?

◀◀
Exercise 11
on page 35

E Pat plays the same game with 3 balls.

Only one ball will fit in each basket.

Which three baskets could Pat's balls go in to make 15?

◀◀
Exercise 8
on page 31

F 1. Rita had 6 large pots and 9 small pots.

How many pots did she have altogether?

2. Tina had 8 large plants and 7 small plants.

How many plants did she have altogether?

◀◀
Exercise 9
on page 34

G Add these.

1. 4 + 3 + 6	2. 3 + 8 + 7	3. 2 + 8 + 5
4. 8 + 3 + 8	5. 5 + 4 + 7	6. 6 + 3 + 5
7. 9 + 6 + 2	8. 4 + 0 + 13	9. 11 + 4 + 3
10. 12 + 6 + 2	11. 14 + 1 + 4	12. 8 + 9 + 2

13.   4   14.   9   15.   7
      11   11   6
    + 3   + 0   + 5

◀◀
Exercise 10
on page 35

H This is a magic square.

Use a copy of this.

Fill in the missing numbers.

6		
	5	9
	4	

Quick Test 1

Mrs Patel put her 5 cats in the cat show.
Each cat had a number.

A How many tens are in these numbers?

1. 463   2. 486   3. 453

B What is the value of the 9?

1. 497   2. 479

C Mrs Patel had to write out
a card like this for each cat.

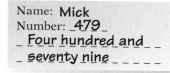

Name: Mick
Number: _479_
_ Four hundred and _ _
_ seventy nine _ _ _ _ _

Use a copy of these.
Fill them in.

1.
Name: Cass
Number: _486_
_ _ _ _ _ _ _ _ _ _ _ _ _
_ _ _ _ _ _ _ _ _ _ _ _ _

2.
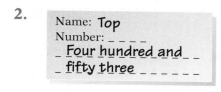
Name: Top
Number: _ _ _ _
_ Four hundred and _ _
_ fifty three _ _ _ _ _ _

D The cats were put in order.
Put these numbers in order from smallest to biggest.

479   453   463   497   486

E The cats were given points.
These were written on a card.

Mick	Top	Kitty	Cass	Fat Cat
9 +8	13 +5	11 +6	12 +8	9 +11

How many points altogether did these get?

1. Mick   2. Top   3. Kitty   4. Cass   5. Fat Cat

4 Subtracting

Selling...

Simon has 9 sheep   He sells 6   He has 3 sheep left

Draw pictures like the 3 above to show these.
- A shop has ten TVs. Four are sold.
- A shop has nine hats. Five are sold.
- A dog has seven puppies. Four are sold.

Subtracting with numbers up to 10

Remember . . .

You should know the **subtraction facts** to 10.
This addition table may help.

+	0	1	2	3	4	5	6	7	8	9	10
0	0	1	2	3	4	5	6	7	8	9	10
1	1	2	3	4	5	6	7	8	9	10	
2	2	3	4	5	6	7	8	9	10		
3	3	4	5	6	7	8	9	10			
4	4	5	6	7	8	9	10				
5	5	6	7	8	9	10					

Examples   7 – 4 = 3   7 – 3 = 4

When we **subtract zero** the number stays the same.

Examples $7 - 0 = 7$ $9 - 0 = 9$ $8 - 0 = 8$

Exercise 1   **A** Find the answers to these.

1. $5 - 3$ 2. $7 - 2$ 3. $4 - 3$
4. $6 - 1$ 5. $4 - 2$ 6. $5 - 2$
7. $10 - 3$ 8. $10 - 4$ 9. $10 - 6$
10. $8 - 3$ 11. $9 - 4$ 12. $9 - 5$
13. $10 - 0$ 14. $8 - 0$ 15. $10 - 7$
16. $\begin{array}{r} 9 \\ -\,3 \\ \hline \end{array}$ 17. $\begin{array}{r} 10 \\ -\,5 \\ \hline \end{array}$ 18. $\begin{array}{r} 8 \\ -\,5 \\ \hline \end{array}$
19. $\begin{array}{r} 7 \\ -\,6 \\ \hline \end{array}$ 20. $\begin{array}{r} 6 \\ -\,0 \\ \hline \end{array}$

B What number goes in the box?

1. $7 - \square = 4$ 2. $6 - \square = 4$ 3. $5 - \square = 3$
4. $8 - \square = 5$ 5. $9 - \square = 6$ 6. $10 - \square = 8$
7. $7 - \square = 2$ 8. $10 - \square = 3$ 9. $9 - \square = 5$
10. $\square - 3 = 2$ 11. $\square - 4 = 1$ 12. $\square - 1 = 3$
13. $\square - 2 = 6$ 14. $\square - 3 = 7$ 15. $\square - 4 = 4$
16. $\square - 3 = 3$ 17. $\square - 5 = 5$ 18. $\square - 6 = 3$

C

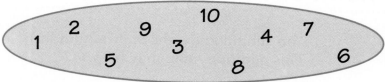

1. $\square - \square = 2$
   Find 4 ways to fill in the boxes.
   Choose numbers from the ring.

2. $\square - \square = 3$
   Find 4 ways to fill in the boxes.
   Choose numbers from the ring.

3. $\square - \square = 4$
   Find as many ways as you can to fill in the boxes.
   Choose numbers from the ring.

Exercise 2   **A**   1.   Jo had 5 sweets. She ate 2.
How many were left?

2.   Ben had 9 sweets. He ate 4.
How many were left?

3.   Sam had 8 sweets. He ate 3.
How many were left?

B   1.   Kath had 6 kittens. She gave 4 away.
How many were left?

2.   Misa had 10 kittens. She gave 6 away.
How many were left?

3.   Sue had 8 kittens. She gave 5 away.
How many were left?

C   1.   Sara had £9. She spent £3.
How much did she have left?

2.   Bob had £7. He spent £4.
How much did he have left?

3.   Deri had £10. He spent £3.
How much did he have left?

D   1.   Pat had 8 roses. She gave 4 away.
How many were left?

2.   Lisa had 7 roses. She gave 3 away.
How many were left?

3.   John had 6 roses. He gave none away.
How many were left?

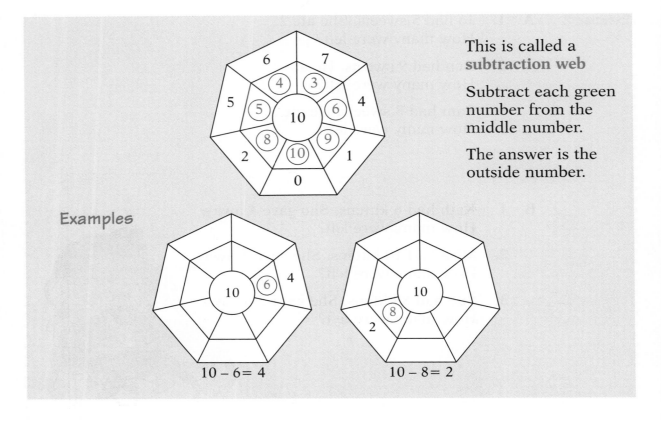

This is called a **subtraction web**

Subtract each green number from the middle number.

The answer is the outside number.

Examples

10 − 6 = 4

10 − 8 = 2

Exercise 3

Use a copy of these subtraction webs.

Fill them in.

1.

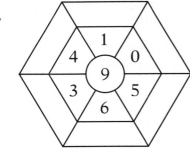

2.

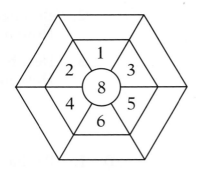

3.

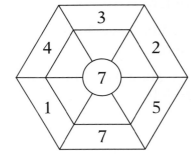

4.

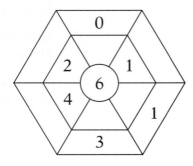

Game for 2 players: THREE IN A ROW

You will need
a dice
red counters
green counters
this board

4	7	6	8	7	5
5	9	5	7	8	9
6	8	6	4	6	5
9	4	7	9	8	4

To play
- Take turns to toss the dice.
- Subtract the number on the dice from 10.
- Put a counter on this number.

Example   Sam tossed a 6.

10 - 6 = 4

Sam put his counter on a 4.

- The winner is the first person to get 3 counters in a line.

Examples

●	●	●	8	7	5
5	9	5	7	8	9
6	8	6	4	6	5
9	4	7	9	8	4

or

4	●	6	8	7	5
5	●	5	7	8	9
6	●	6	4	6	5
9	4	7	9	8	4

or

4	7	6	8	●	5
5	9	5	●	8	9
6	8	●	4	6	5
9	4	7	9	8	4

or

●	7	6	8	7	5
5	●	5	7	8	9
6	8	●	4	6	5
9	4	7	9	8	4

Subtracting with numbers up to 20

Learn the subtraction facts up to 20.
This addition table may help.

+	0	1	2	3	4	5	6	7	8	9	10	11	12	13	14	15	16	17	18	19	20
0	0	1	2	3	4	5	6	7	8	9	10	11	12	13	14	15	16	17	18	19	20
1	1	2	3	4	5	6	7	8	9	10	11	12	13	14	15	16	17	18	19	20	
2	2	3	4	5	6	7	8	9	10	11	12	13	14	15	16	17	18	19	20		
3	3	4	5	6	7	8	9	10	11	12	13	14	15	16	17	18	19	20			
4	4	5	6	7	8	9	10	11	12	13	14	15	16	17	18	19	20				
5	5	6	7	8	9	10	11	12	13	14	15	16	17	18	19	20					
6	6	7	8	9	10	11	12	13	14	15	16	17	18	19	20						
7	7	8	9	10	11	12	13	14	15	16	17	18	19	20							
8	8	9	10	11	12	13	14	15	16	17	18	19	20								
9	9	10	11	12	13	14	15	16	17	18	19	20									
10	10	11	12	13	14	15	16	17	18	19	20										

Examples $18 - 7 = 11$ $18 - 11 = 7$

A way to help you work out subtractions

Use the addition facts.

$18 - 7 = \boxed{}$

To find what goes in the box we say $7 + \boxed{?} = 18$.

We know $7 + \boxed{11} = 18$.

So $18 - 7 = \boxed{11}$

Examples $19 - 6 = \boxed{}$ $17 - 11 = \boxed{}$

We know $6 + \boxed{13} = 19$.   We know $11 + 6 = 17$.

So $19 - 6 = \boxed{13}$ So $17 - 11 = 6$

Use the addition facts to find the answers to these.

$17 - 5 = \boxed{}$ $18 - 9 = \boxed{}$ $19 - 7 = \boxed{}$

$19 - 11 = \boxed{}$ $15 - 6 = \boxed{}$

Exercise 4   **A**   Write down the answers to these.

1.	16 – 10	2.	12 – 6	3.	11 – 2
4.	17 – 10	5.	19 – 2	6.	20 – 4
7.	16 – 3	8.	17 – 4	9.	19 – 9
10.	15 – 3	11.	13 – 3	12.	11 – 3
13.	16 – 5	14.	12 – 9	15.	20 – 6
16.	14 – 5	17.	19 – 11	18.	17 – 0
19.	15 – 6	20.	20 – 7	21.	19 – 8
22.	18 – 7	23.	15 – 9	24.	18 – 12

25.   20
     – 12

26.   16
     – 11

27.   18
     – 11

28.   17
     – 13

29.   20
     – 11

B   What number goes in the box?

1. $12 - \square = 6$ 2. $14 - \square = 8$ 3. $17 - \square = 12$
4. $19 - \square = 11$ 5. $18 - \square = 7$ 6. $20 - \square = 9$
7. $16 - \square = 9$ 8. $15 - \square = 6$ 9. $19 - \square = 7$
10. $15 - \square = 15$ 11. $17 - \square = 5$

Exercise 5   Five of these subtractions are *not* true.
Write down the letters which are beside these.
Make a word from these letters.

P	11 – 6 = 5	E	17 – 12 = 5	N	18 – 7 = 11
L	20 – 11 = 9	F	20 – 11 = 9	M	19 – 5 = 13
B	18 – 5 = 13	T	19 – 8 = 12	O	15 – 15 = 0
A	19 – 7 = 11	Q	16 – 7 = 9	H	17 – 11 = 5
I	17 – 9 = 8	S	15 – 9 = 4	R	20 – 9 = 11

Exercise 6   Use a copy of these subtraction webs.
Fill them in.

1.
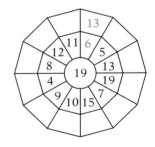

2.
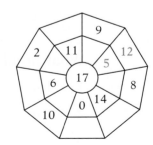

Example   Jill made 19 buns. She ate 7.

How many were left?

Answer   19 − 7 = 12

12 were left.

Exercise 7   **A**   How much are these now?

1.

was £18

£10 off

now _____

2.

was £20

£11 off

now _____

3.

was £17

£8 off

now _____

B   1.   Sara had 17 books. She sold 11.

How many were left?

2.   Mindu had 20 books. He sold 12.

How many were left?

3.   Claire had 19 books. She sold 8.

How many were left?

C   These are the entries in a fishing contest.

FISHING CONTEST	FISHING CONTEST	FISHING CONTEST
Name: Kim Brown	Name: Jon Dean	Name: Mary Chan
Age: 9	Age: 17	Age: 13

What number goes in the gap?

1.   Jon is _____ years older than Kim.

2.   Jon is _____ years older than Mary.

3.   Mary is _____ years older than Kim.

D Jim played a game with darts.
He threw a dart and subtracted the number from 20.
What did he get in these games?

1.    **2.** 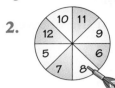   **3.**

E Some friends played a game.
They rolled balls down a hill.
They wrote down how far each rolled.

Dipta	19 metres	Jane	13 metres
Roy	11 metres	Sam	5 metres
Helen	8 metres	Pam	17 metres

What number goes in the gap?

1. Dipta's ball rolled _____ metres more than Jane's.
2. Pam's ball rolled _____ metres more than Helen's.
3. Pam's ball rolled _____ metres more than Roy's.
4. Jane's ball rolled _____ metres more than Sam's.

Investigation

● Copy these. Write down the answers.

$9 - 5 =$	$11 - 3 =$	$13 - 5 =$
$15 - 5 =$	$17 - 7 =$	$19 - 3 =$
$11 - 7 =$	$19 - 13 =$	$17 - 9 =$

Copy this sentence. Fill in the gap.

*When we subtract an odd number from an odd number we get
an _____ number.*

● Find out what happens when you subtract an even number from
an even number.

● Find out what happens when you subtract an odd number from
an even number.

Homework/Review 1

A Write down the answer to these.

1.	11 – 3	2.	12 – 5	3.	14 – 6

1. 11 – 3
2. 12 – 5
3. 14 – 6
4. 15 – 4
5. 18 – 4
6. 19 – 5
7. 17 – 2
8. 20 – 5
9. 13 – 0
10. 18 – 7
11. 19 – 8
12. 17 – 8
13. 20 – 11
14. 16 – 11
15. 19 – 13

16.   15
   – 8

17.   17
  – 12

18.   18
  – 11

19.   17
  – 9

20.   20
  – 7

B Bethan played a game with cubes.

The number on the green cube was subtracted from the number on the white cube.

What did she get in these games?

1.
2.
3.
4.

C How can you make an egg run faster?

Use a copy of the box.

O   19 – 5 = 14
I   20 – 12
E   18 – 7
N   19 – 12
T   20 – 7
Y   18 – 12
U   15 – 0
G   20 – 11

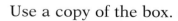

O					
6	14	15	11	9	9

		O	
8	13	14	7

Adding and subtracting

Sometimes we have to add and sometimes we have to subtract.
Look at the sign carefully.

Exercise 8   **A** Write down the answers to these.

1. 7 + 3	2. 11 – 3	3. 12 – 5
4. 7 + 9	5. 16 – 5	6. 8 + 6
7. 12 + 8	8. 20 – 11	9. 13 + 5
10. 19 – 5	11. 12 + 0	12. 13 – 7
13. 15 – 8	14. 16 + 3	15. 14 + 5
16. 13 + 6	17. 17 – 0	18. 19
19. 11	20. 16	– 7
+ 4	– 9	

B What number goes in the box?

1. 14 + ☐ = 19   2. 19 – ☐ = 12   3. 14 – ☐ = 5
4. 11 + ☐ = 19   5. 16 – ☐ = 5   6. 7 + ☐ = 16
7. 17 – ☐ = 9   8. 20 – ☐ = 11   9. 9 + ☐ = 20
10. ☐ + 5 = 13   11. ☐ – 5 = 12   12. ☐ + 6 = 17
13. ☐ – 4 = 12   14. ☐ + 3 = 19   15. ☐ – 9 = 7
16. ☐ + 11 = 20   17. ☐ – 8 = 9

Exercise 9   Choose two numbers from the ring that **add** or **subtract** to give 11.
Do this in as many ways as you can.
One way is 20 – 9 = 11.

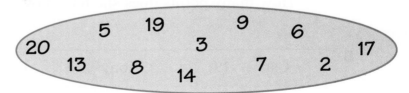

Sometimes we have to work out if we add or subtract.

Example   Ross had £12. He lost £5.
How much did he have then?

Answer   We have to subtract.
12 – 5 = 7.
Ross had £7.

Example   Ted had 11 points in a game. He got 7 more.
           How many points did he have then?

Answer   We have to add.
           11 + 7 = 18.
           Ted had 18 points.

Exercise 10   **A**   This is part of a game board.

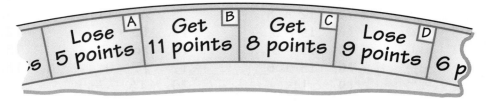

1. Don had 13 points.
   He landed on square A.
   How many points does he have now?

2. Pip had 11 points.
   She landed on square C.
   How many points does she have now?

3. Sally had 17 points.
   She landed on square D.
   How many points does she have now?

4. Nesta had 7 points
   She landed on square B.
   How many points does she have now?

B

Carl	19	Tony	8
Bob	14	Adam	20

In a game if you spin black you get 6 more points.
If you spin green you lose 5 points.
How many points would these have after this spin?

1. Carl spins green.   2. Tony spins black.

3. Bob spins black.   4. Adam spins green.

Homework/Review 2

A Find the answer to these.

1. 7 + 4	2. 12 − 3	3. 13 − 5
4. 8 + 9	5. 15 − 4	6. 18 − 9
7. 11 + 9	8. 20 − 9	9. 14 + 5
10. 19 − 4	11. 13 + 0	12. 15 − 7
13. 12 + 7	14. 18 − 0	15. $\begin{array}{r} 12 \\ + 6 \\ \hline \end{array}$
16. $\begin{array}{r} 18 \\ - 7 \\ \hline \end{array}$	17. $\begin{array}{r} 17 \\ - 11 \\ \hline \end{array}$	

B What number goes in the box?

1. 8 + ☐ = 14   2. 12 − ☐ = 5   3. 15 − ☐ = 8
4. 9 + ☐ = 17   5. 14 − ☐ = 6   6. 8 + ☐ = 19
7. ☐ + 5 = 16   8. ☐ − 7 = 5   9. ☐ − 9 = 11
10. ☐ − 4 = 13   11. ☐ − 8 = 12

C Choose two numbers from the ring that **add** or **subtract** to 12.
Do this in as many ways as you can.
One way is 20 − 8 = 12.

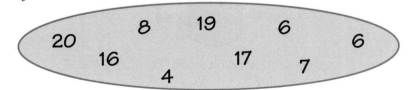

20   16   8   4   19   17   6   7   6

D **When are you most likely to dream about ice-cream?**

Use a copy of the box.

E	9 + 6 = 15	R	20 − 11
O	12 − 4	Y	11 + 7
W	12 + 5	H	19 − 13
A	18 − 5	L	17 − 12
N	19 − 5	S	11 + 5
U	7 + 0	P	16 − 5

$$\overline{17} \;\; \overline{6} \;\; \overset{E}{\overline{15}} \;\; \overline{14}$$

$$\overline{18} \;\; \overline{8} \;\; \overline{7}$$

$$\overline{13} \;\; \overline{9} \;\; \overset{E}{\overline{15}}$$

$$\overline{13} \;\; \overline{16} \;\; \overline{5} \;\; \overset{E}{\overline{15}} \;\; \overset{E}{\overline{15}} \;\; \overline{11}$$

Game for 2 or more players: MAKE 15

You will need a dice

To play
- All players start with 10 points.
- Take turns to toss the dice.
- Add **or** subtract the number you toss to your points.
- The first person to get 15 points wins.

Example Liz tossed on her first turn.

She added it to 10.   10 + 3 = 13.

She tossed on her next turn.

She added it to 13.   13 + 5 = 18.

She tossed on her next turn.

She subtracted it from 18.   18 − 1 = 17.

She tossed on her next turn.

She subtracted it from 17.   17 − 2 = 15.

- Play this game 10 times.

◄◄ CHAPTER REVIEW ◄◄

Exercise 1
on page 42

A Write down the answers to these.

1. 6 − 3   2. 7 − 4   3. 10 − 3
4. 9 − 5   5. 10 − 7   6. 8 − 5

◄◄

Exercise 2
on page 43

B **1.** Ben had 9 sweets. He ate 4.

How many were left?

2. Maria had 10 sweets. She ate 7.

How many were left?

◄◄

Exercise 4
on page 47

C Subtract these.

1. 17 – 10	**2.** 13 – 6	**3.** 12 – 5
4. 16 – 4	**5.** 17 – 3	**6.** 20 – 5
7. 18 – 2	**8.** 19 – 4	**9.** 13 – 8
10. 11 – 3	**11.** 16 – 9	**12.** 17 – 11
13. 19 – 12	**14.** 20 – 11	**15.** 18
16. 15	**17.** 17	– 12
– 9	– 12	

◄◄

Exercise 7
on page 48

D Don plays a game at a fair.

He throws a dart at the green board.

He throws another dart at the white board.

He subtracts white from green.

What did he get in these games?

1. 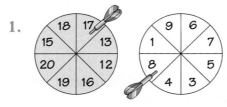   **2.**

◄◄

Exercise 8
on page 51

E Find the answers to these.

1. 8 + 6	**2.** 17 – 4	**3.** 9 + 8
4. 14 – 5	**5.** 12 + 5	**6.** 11 – 4
7. 19 – 11	**8.** 8 + 12	**9.** 7 + 11

◄◄

Exercise 9
on page 51

F Choose two numbers from the box that **add** or **subtract** to give 9.

Do this as many ways as you can.

One way is 15 – 6 = 9.

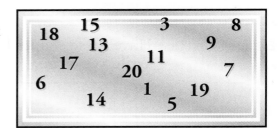

5 Halves and Quarters

Games..

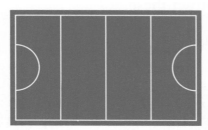

A hockey field is cut into parts.

Draw some other fields that games are played on.
How many parts are there?

Draw a field of your own that a game could be played on.
Make up some rules for the game.

Halves

When we cut something in **half** we get 2 bits.
Both bits are exactly the same.
Each bit is called **one half**.
We write this as $\frac{1}{2}$.

Example   The dashed line cuts each
of these in half.

Exercise 1   Have these shapes been cut in half by the dashed line?
Write **yes** or **no**.

1. 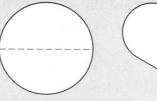   2.   3.

4.   5.   6.

Exercise 2   Four of these shapes have half shaded.

Write down the letters which are beside these.

Make a word from the four letters.

One half or $\frac{1}{2}$ means 1 out of every 2.

Example   Shade half of these cats.

Answer   We must shade 1 out of every 2.

So **3** cats are shaded and **3** are not.

Exercise 3

Use a copy of these.

Shade half of them.

The first one is done.

1.

2.

3.

4.

5.

6.

When 2 people share something equally, they get $\frac{1}{2}$ each.

Example Brad and Lisa ate half of these each.
How many did they each eat?

Answer There are 6 cakes.

Half of 6 is 3.

Each ate 3 cakes.

Exercise 4   **A**   Brad and Lisa won a hamper of food.

They shared all the things equally.

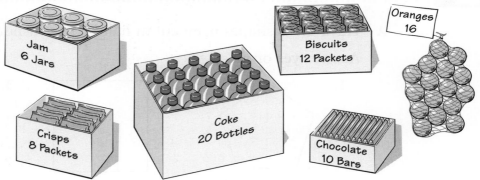

How many of these did each get?

1. jars of jam   2. packets of biscuits
3. oranges   4. packets of crisps
5. bottles of Coke   6. bars of chocolate

B   Two brothers shared a farm.

They each owned half of these.

8 pigs   18 hens
12 sheep   14 cows
6 horses   16 ducks

How many of these did each own?

1. pigs   2. sheep   3. horses
4. hens   5. cows   6. ducks

C   Two sisters shared their clothes.

Together they had 20 dresses and 16 tops.

Each owned half.

1. How many dresses did each own?

2. How many tops did each own?

Homework/Review 1

A   Have these shapes been cut in half by the dashed line?

Answer **yes** or **no**.

1.   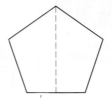   2.      3.

B   Use a copy of these.

Shade half.

1.

2.

C   Two netball teams shared this afternoon tea.

They both got the same.

      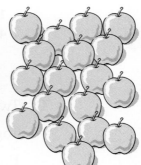

How many of these did each team get?

1.   biscuits   2.   Cola   3.   apples

Puzzle

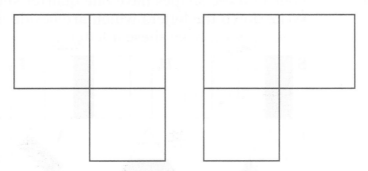

Use a copy of these two shapes.
Cut them out.
Pam put the two bits together to make this shape.

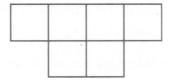

How many other shapes can you make?

40	Excellent
35	Very very good
25	Very good
20	Good
10	Keep trying

Quarters

When we cut something into
quarters we get 4 bits.
All 4 bits are exactly the same.
Each bit is called **one quarter**.

We write this as $\frac{1}{4}$.

Example   One quarter of this shape is shaded.

Exercise 5   Four of these shapes have one quarter shaded.
Write down the letters which are beside these.
Make a word from these 4 letters.

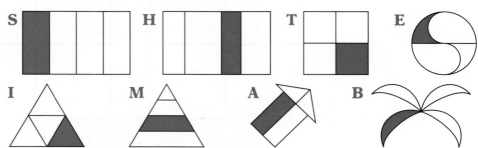

One quarter or $\frac{1}{4}$ means 1 out of every 4.

Example   Shade one quarter of these triangles.

Answer   We must shade 1 out of every 4.

So we must shade 2.

Does it matter which 2 we shade?

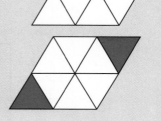

Exercise 6   Use a copy of this.
Shade a quarter.
The first one is done.

1.

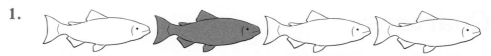

2.

3.

4.

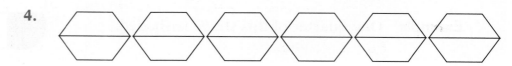

Example   Four friends shared 12 bananas.
One quarter of 12 is 3.
They each got 3.

Exercise 7   **A**   A family of 4 bought a family meal.

1. How many pieces of pizza did each get?
2. How many baby potatoes did each get?
3. How many pieces of chicken did each get?
4. How many pots of salad did each get?
5. How many rum balls did each get?

Family Meal

8 pieces of chicken
4 pieces of pizza
16 baby potatoes
12 pots of salad
20 rum balls

B   Four children at a party shared this food equally.

20 sweets   12 bits of pizza   8 small bags of crisps
  4 bottles of cola   16 biscuits

What number goes in the gap?

1. Each got __ sweets.   2. Each got __ bits of pizza.
3. Each got __ bags of crisps. 4. Each got __ bottle of cola.
5. Each got __ biscuits.

What fraction?

Example   What fraction of these is shaded?

Answer   Two out of eight are shaded.
We can put them into groups.

1 in every 4 is shaded.
So $\frac{1}{4}$ is shaded.

Exercise 8   What fraction is shaded?

1.

2.

3.

4.

5.

6. ★☆☆★☆☆★☆☆☆☆☆

7. ○●●○○●○●○○●●○●

8. ▲△△△▲△△△△△△▲△△▲△

Example   Ben had 8 sweets.
He ate 4.
What fraction did he eat?

Answer   Ben ate 4 out of 8.
This is $\frac{1}{2}$.

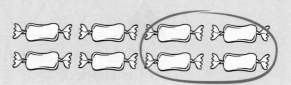

Exercise 9   Lucy and Penny went to a party.

A   There were 8 prizes.

    1.   Lucy won 4 of them.
        What fraction is this?

    2.   Penny won 2 of them.
        What fraction is this?

B   There were 12 bits of pizza.

    1.   Lucy ate 3 of them.
        What fraction is this?

    2.   Penny ate 6 of them.
        What fraction is this?

Homework/Review 2

A   Use a copy of this.
Shade one quarter.

    1.

    2.

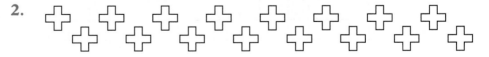

B   Four friends won these.

They shared the things equally.

    1.   How many pies did each get?

    2.   How many chocolate bars did each get?

    3.   How many packets of crisps did each get?

C Lucy and Penny played a game.

They each threw 12 darts at a board.

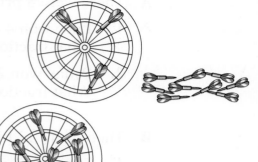

1. What fraction of Lucy's darts hit the board?

2. What fraction of Penny's darts hit the board?

Investigation

 One half of this shape has been shaded.

Use some copies of each of these.
Shade one half.
Find as many ways as you can.

  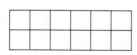   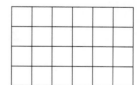

 One quarter of this has been shaded.

Use some copies of each of these.
Shade one quarter.
Find as many ways as you can.

      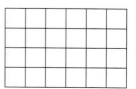

◀◀ CHAPTER REVIEW ◀◀

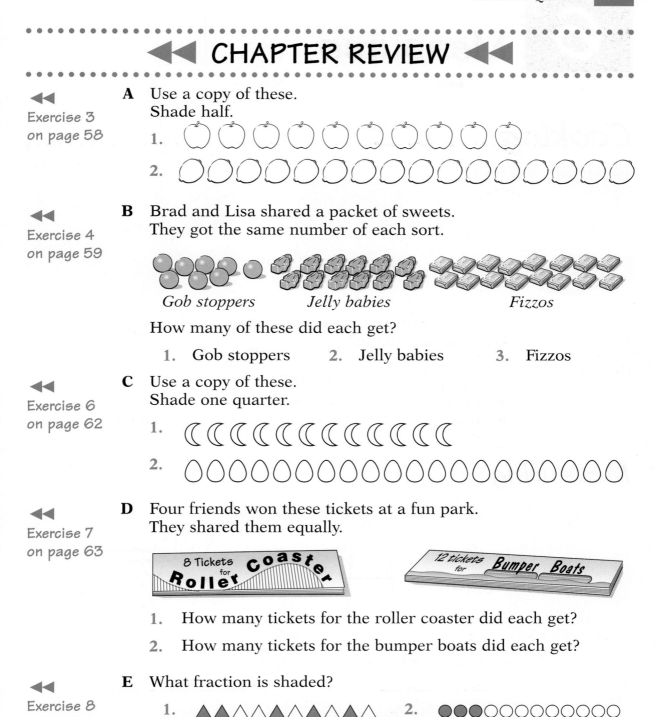

◀◀
Exercise 3
on page 58

A Use a copy of these.
Shade half.

1.

2.

◀◀
Exercise 4
on page 59

B Brad and Lisa shared a packet of sweets.
They got the same number of each sort.

Gob stoppers　　　*Jelly babies*　　　*Fizzos*

How many of these did each get?

1. Gob stoppers　　2. Jelly babies　　3. Fizzos

◀◀
Exercise 6
on page 62

C Use a copy of these.
Shade one quarter.

1.

2.

◀◀
Exercise 7
on page 63

D Four friends won these tickets at a fun park.
They shared them equally.

8 Tickets for **Roller Coaster**

12 tickets for **Bumper Boats**

1. How many tickets for the roller coaster did each get?

2. How many tickets for the bumper boats did each get?

◀◀
Exercise 8
on page 64

E What fraction is shaded?

1. ▲▲△△▲△▲△▲△　　2. ●●●○○○○○○○

◀◀
Exercise 9
on page 65

F Bob had 16 chocolates.
He ate 8 of them.
What fraction did he eat?

6 Measures

Cooking..

When we cook we use these to measure with.
What else do we use?

What could we use to measure these?

- butter
- flour
- milk
- sauce
- meat
- sugar

Measuring

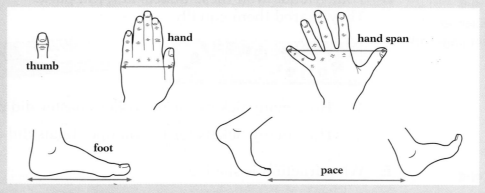

We could use these to measure with.

Example   This page is about 12 of my thumbs across.

Measure this page with your thumb.
Did you get the same answer?

Task 1

Use a copy of this.

A Use your thumb to measure some things.

Fill in the table.

Did everyone get the same answers?

What I measured	Number of thumbs
how wide my desk is	
how long my pencil is	

B Use your hand span to measure some things.

Fill in the table.

What I measured	Number of hand spans
how high the door is	
how wide a window is	

Did everyone get the same answers?

C Use paces to measure some things.

Fill in the table.

Did everyone get the same answers?

What I measured	Number of paces
how long the room is	
how wide the room is	

D Use your foot to measure some things.

Fill in the table.

Did everyone get the same answers?

What I measured	Number of feet
how long the room is	
how wide the room is	

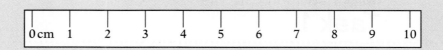

We use a ruler to measure in **centimetres**.
cm is short for centimetre.

Example

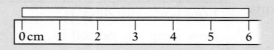

We put the end of the rod at 0.
This rod is 6 cm long.

Exercise 1

How long are these?

1.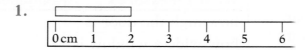

2.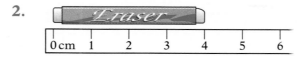

3.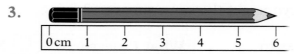

4.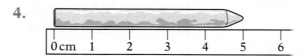

Sometimes the length is not an exact number of centimetres.

Then we read to the nearest mark.

Example

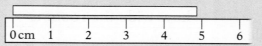

This rod is **about** 5 cm long.

Sometimes the length is close to halfway in between the numbers.

Example

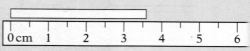

This rod is **about** $3\frac{1}{2}$ cm long.

Exercise 2   About how long are these?

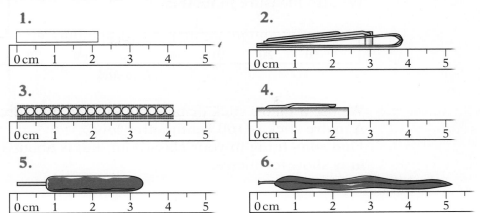

Exercise 3   Measure these lines with your ruler.

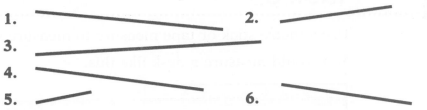

1.
3.
4.
5.
2.
6.

Task 2

Use a ruler to measure some things in centimetres.
When you measure, remember to start at 0.

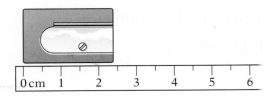

Make a copy of this table.
Fill it in.

Did everyone get the same answers?

What I measured	Number of centimetres
pencil sharpener	
pencil	

We also measure in **metres**.

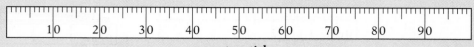

metre stick

We use a metre stick or tape measure to measure in **metres**.
A metre stick is 100 centimetres long.
Find something in your classroom that is about 1 metre.
m is short for metre.

Task 3

Use a metre stick or tape measure to measure some things.

You would measure a desk like this.

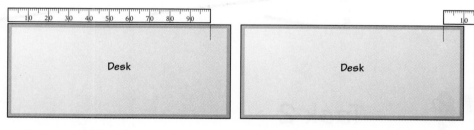

Put a mark where the
metre sticks ends.

Measure the rest
in centimetres.

This desk is 1 metre and 10 centimetres long.

Make a copy of this table.

Fill it in.

What I measured	Number of metres and centimetres
length of desk	

Did everyone get the same answers?

Sometimes we use **feet** or **inches** to measure how long
something is.

Examples   A door is about 7 feet high.
This book is about 7 inches wide.

Exercise 4   **1.**   Write down 3 things we could measure in feet.

2.   Write down 3 things we could measure in inches.

When we want to know how heavy something is, we can
measure in **kilograms**.
kg is short for kilograms.

Example   Jane weighs 54 kg.

Exercise 5   About how heavy are these?

1.    **2.**    **3.**

4.    **5.**    **6.**

7.    **8.**    **9.**

Sometimes we use **pounds** when we want to know how heavy something is.
lb is short for pounds.

Exercise 6   Write down 3 things we could weigh in pounds.

When we want to know how much water something will hold we measure in **litres**.
l is short for litres.

Example   A bucket holds about 5 *l* of water.

Exercise 7   About how much water is in these?

1.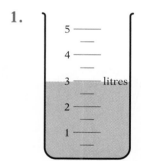

2.

3.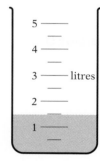

4.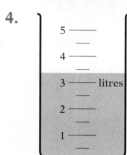

5.

6.

Sometimes we use **pints** instead of litres.

Exercise 8   Write down 3 things we could measure in pints.

Homework/Review 1

A About how long are these rods?

1.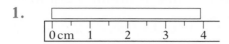

2.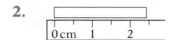

B Measure these pencils.

1.

2.

3.

4.

C Measure the length of your bedroom in paces.

D About how heavy are these?

1.

2.

3.

E About how much water is in these?

1.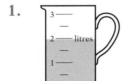

2.

3.

F

metres	centimetres	litres	pints	kilograms	pounds

What words go in the gaps?
Choose from the box.

1. We measure how long something is in _____ or _____ .

2. We measure how heavy something is in _____ or _____ .

3. We measure how much water something can hold in
   _____ or _____ .

Estimating

An **estimate** is a good guess.

Example   Jim estimated that this line is about 5 cm long.

_____

Is Jim right?

Exercise 9   Estimate how long these are.

Check with your ruler.

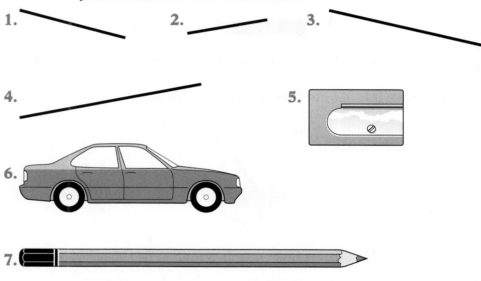

1.

2.

3.

4.

5.

6.

7.

Task 4

A   You will need some newspaper.

1.   Make a pile of newspaper that you think is about one kilogram.

Check to see if you are right.

2.   Make a pile of newspaper that you think is about two kilograms.

Check to see if you are right.

B

Choose two of these.

Fill the smaller one with water.

Tip it into the bigger one.

Estimate how many times you will need to do this to fill the bigger one.

Check to see if you are right.

C You will need a tape measure.

1. Estimate how far a metre is.
   Check to see if you are right.

2. Estimate how many centimetres it is around your head.
   Check to see if you are right.

3. Estimate how long your classroom is.
   Check to see if you are right.

4. Estimate how tall a friend is.
   Check to see if you are right.

D You will need a trundle wheel.

1. Estimate how far it is from your classroom to another classroom.

   Check to see if you are right using the trundle wheel. Each time a trundle wheel clicks you have gone one metre.

2. Estimate how far it is from the school gate to a classroom.

   Check to see if you are right.

Exercise 10

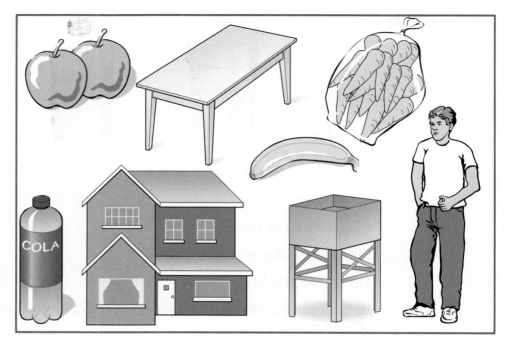

Choose something from the box that could

1. be about 2 m long
2. be about 20 cm long
3. weigh about 2 kg
4. hold about $1\frac{1}{2}$ litres
5. be about 6 m high
6. be about $1\frac{1}{2}$ m high
7. hold about 200 litres
8. weigh about $\frac{1}{2}$ pound.

Exercise 11

1	5	10	20	50	200	1000

What goes in the gap?

Choose from the box.

1. A room could be about _____ metres long.
2. A book could be about _____ centimetres across.
3. A bath could hold about _____ litres.
4. A jug could hold about _____ litre of milk.
5. A school could be about _____ metres high.
6. A car could weigh about _____ kilograms.
7. A person could weigh about _____ kilograms.

Homework/Review 2

A Estimate how long these lines are.

Check with your ruler.

1.

2.

3.

4.

B **How do hikers dress on cold mornings?**

		E					E		
5 *l*	2 m	50 km	2 kg		5 *l*	2 m	50 km	2 kg
2 cm	20 cm	20 m	5 km					

Use a copy of the box.

Find the answer from the box that goes in the gap.

The first one is done.

E A bike could be about __2 m__ long.

A A telephone could be about _____ long.

Y A book could weigh about _____ .

T Sam hiked about _____ yesterday.

R Rick went on holiday. He drove about _____ .

S A house could be about _____ long.

F A book could be about _____ thick.

V A bucket could hold about _____ .

Puzzles

1.   Which green line looks longer?

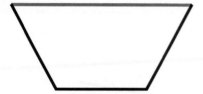 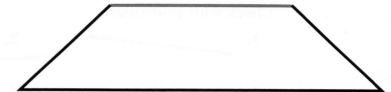

2.   Are the green lines straight?

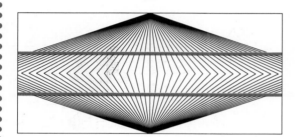 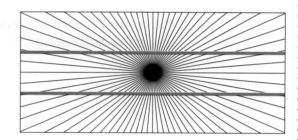

3.   Which green circle is bigger?

4.   Is the green line or the black line longer?

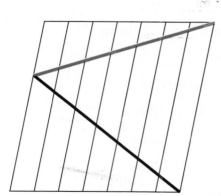

◄◄ CHAPTER REVIEW ◄◄

◄◄

Exercise 2
on page 71

A About how long are these?

1.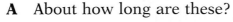

2.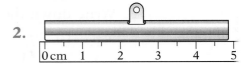

◄◄

Exercise 5
on page 73

B About how heavy are these?

1.

2.

◄◄

Exercise 7
on page 74

C About how much water is in these?

1.    2.   3.

◄◄

Exercise 9
on page 76

D Estimate how long these lines are.

Check with your ruler.

1.

2.

3.

◄◄

Exercise 11
on page 78

E

1	2	3	5	10	40	300	400	500	2000

What number from the box goes in the gap?

1. A door is about _____ metres high.

2. A coffee mug is about _____ centimetres high.

3. A big dog weighs about _____ kilograms.

4. A car is about _____ metres long.

5. Four apples weigh about _____ pounds.

Quick Test 2

A Write down the answers to these.

    1. 19 – 7   **2.** 15 – 9   **3.** 16 – 5

    4. 20 – 11   **5.** 17 – 8

B Glyn was baking for a party.

How much of these did he measure?

    1. sugar   **2.** flour   **3.** butter

C Which of these pictures is about 4 cm wide.

D What number goes in the gap? | 8   45   80 |

Choose from the box.

    1. An oven tray could be about _____ cm long.

    2. A small cake could be about _____ cm wide.

E Use a copy of these.

Draw a cherry on top of half of them.

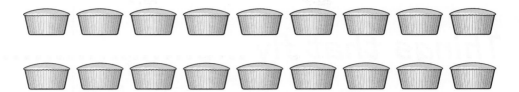

F What fraction of these cakes have cherries around the outside?

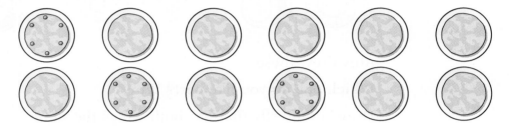

G Glyn made some plates of fudge.

　　1. One plate had 19 bits. 11 were eaten.

　　　　How many were left?

　　2. One plate had 20 bits. 9 were eaten.

　　　　How many were left?

　　3. One plate had 17 bits. 12 were eaten.

　　　　How many were left?

7 Symmetry

Things that fly ....

 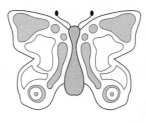 

Amy drew these.

Which one do you like best? Why?

Draw a butterfly that has both wings the same.

Do these have both wings the same?

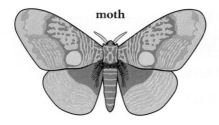
moth

eagle

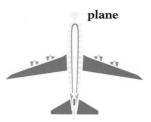
plane

Symmetry

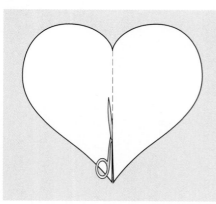

When we cut this shape in half, the two bits are the same.

The shape is **symmetrical**.

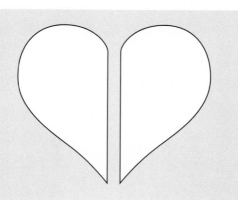

We can use a mirror to see
if a shape is symmetrical.

Task 1

You will need scissors
paper
mirror

A Use a copy of these shapes.
Cut them out.
Try and cut them in half so you get 2 bits the same.
Which ones are symmetrical?

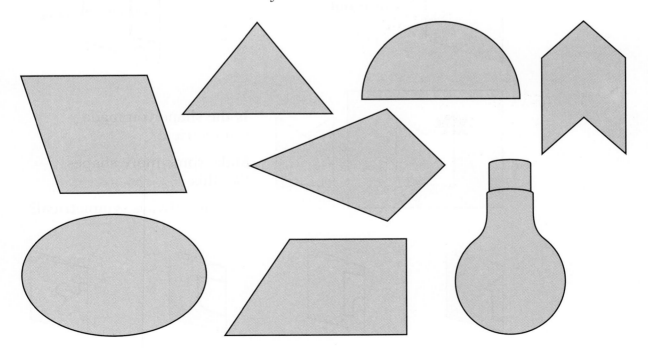

B   Use the mirror to see if these are symmetrical.

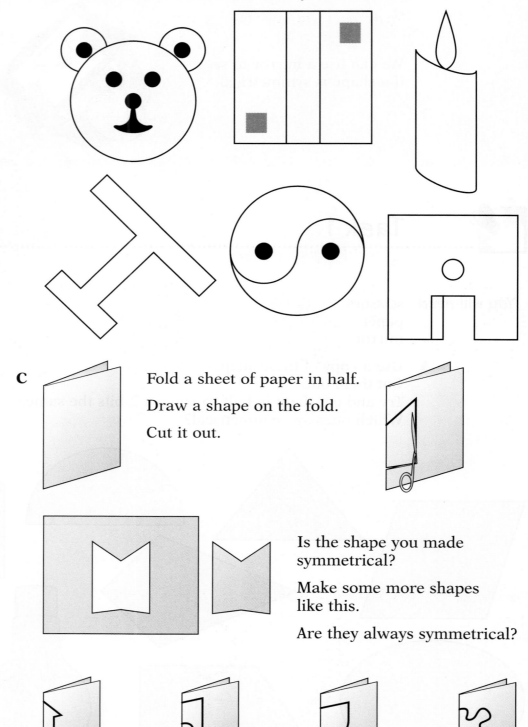

C   Fold a sheet of paper in half.

Draw a shape on the fold.

Cut it out.

Is the shape you made symmetrical?

Make some more shapes like this.

Are they always symmetrical?

Exercise 1 Can these be cut in half to make 2 shapes the same?

Write **yes** or **no** for your answer.

1.

2.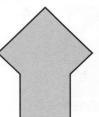

3.

4.

5.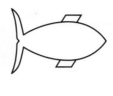

6.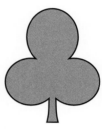

7.

8.

9.

10.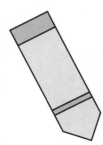

11.

Exercise 2 Which of these shapes is **not** symmetrical?

1.

2.

3.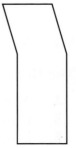

4.

Exercise 3   Are these shapes symmetrical?

Write **yes** or **no** for your answer.

1. 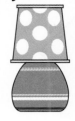   2.    3.    4.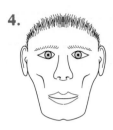

5.    6. 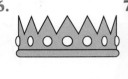   7.    8.

9.    10. 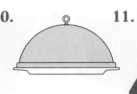   11.    12.

Exercise 4

A   B   C   D   E

V   W   X   Y   Z

What letter goes in the gap?

The first one is done.

1. A matches with ___Y___ .   2. B matches with _____ .
3. C matches with _____ .   4. D matches with _____ .
5. E matches with _____ .

Task 2

You will need   a big sheet of paper or card

Choose one of these.

| flying things | art | masks | the sea | trees |
| patterns | flowers | animals | buildings | photos |

Make a poster about symmetry.

Example   Dipta made this poster.

Game for 2 players: MATCH IT

You will need   the board on the next page

2 red counters
2 green counters
a dice

To play   • Take turns to toss the dice.

• On the first turn put a counter on the **left** of the black line.
Put the counter on the number you tossed.

Example   Ron tossed a 6.

He could put his counter on or

• On the second turn put a counter on the **right** of the black line.
Put the counter on the number you tossed.

• On the next turns, move **one** of your counters to a box that has the number you tossed.

• Always keep the counters on the same side they started on.

• The winner is the first person to make a symmetrical shape.

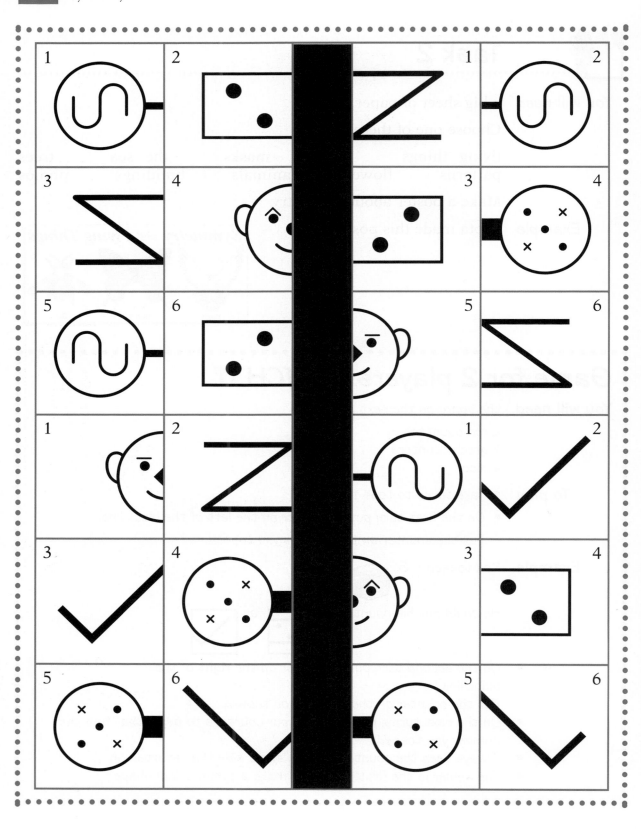

Homework/Review 1

A Can these be cut in half to make 2 shapes the same?

Write **yes** or **no** for your answer.

1.   2.   3.   4.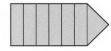

B Use a copy of this.

Shade all the squares that have a symmetrical shape.

C Use a copy of this. Which ones go together? Put a line between them. The first one is done.

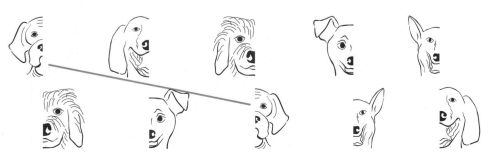

Lines of symmetry

When a shape is symmetrical we can draw a **line of symmetry** on it.

Examples

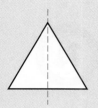 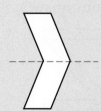  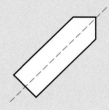

Exercise 5   Is the dashed line a line of symmetry?

1.

2.

3.

4.
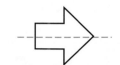

5.

6.

Exercise 6   Use a copy of this.

Draw on the line of symmetry.

The first one is done.

1.
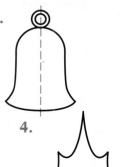

2.

3.

4.

5.
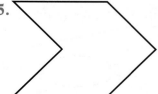

6.
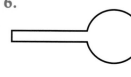

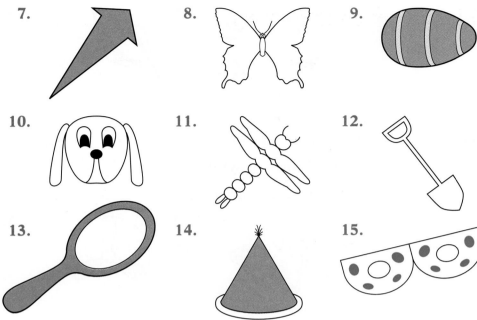

7. 8. 9.

10. 11. 12.

13. 14. 15.

Some shapes have more than one line of symmetry.

Examples

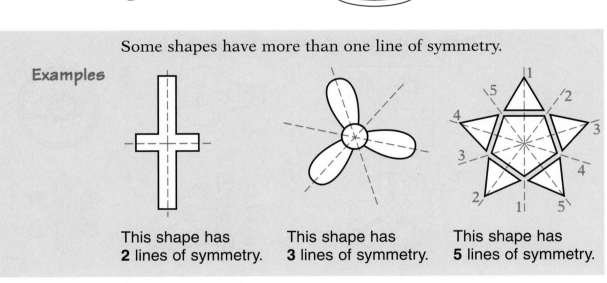

This shape has **2** lines of symmetry.

This shape has **3** lines of symmetry.

This shape has **5** lines of symmetry.

Exercise 7

Use a copy of these.

Draw 2 lines of symmetry on each.

The first one is done.

1. 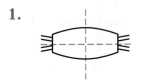   2. 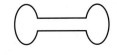   3.

4.   **5.**   **6.**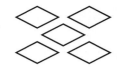

Exercise 8   Use a copy of this.

Draw 3 lines of symmetry on each.

The first one is done.

1. 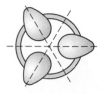   **2.** 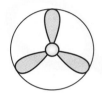   **3.**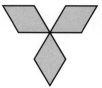

Exercise 9   Use a copy of this.

Draw all the lines of symmetry on each.

1. 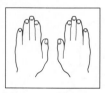   **2.** 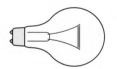   **3.**

4.   **5.** 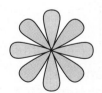   **6.**

7.   **8.** 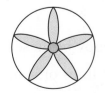   **9.**

10. 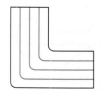   **11.**

Homework/Review 2

A Is the dashed line a line of symmetry?

1.    2. 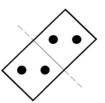   3.

B Use a copy of this.

Draw the line of symmetry on each.

1. 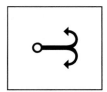   2.    3.

C Use a copy of this.

Draw 2 lines of symmetry on each.

1. 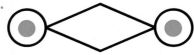   2. 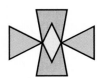   3.

D Use a copy of this.

Draw 3 lines of symmetry on each.

1.   2.   3.

E Use a copy of this.

Draw on **all** the lines of symmetry.

1.   2.   3.

Task 3

You will need scissors
sheets of square paper

A

Fold the paper in half,
then in half again.

Draw a shape
on the folds.

Before you open it, guess how many lines of symmetry your
shape will have.

Make some more shapes like this.

Do they always have the same number of lines of symmetry?

B

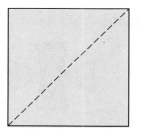   

Fold the paper
in half

Fold it in
half again

Cut out bits
from all
the sides.

Open it out. You have
made a **snowflake**.
How many lines of
symmetry does it have?

 Investigation

A B C D E F G H I
J K L M N O P Q
R S T U V W X Y Z

How many lines of symmetry does each of these letters have?
Use letters like these to write your name.
Draw the lines of symmetry on each letter.
How many are there altogether?

- The word MUM is symmetrical.

Try to find some other words that are symmetrical.

Puzzle

Use a mirror to read this.

in it.

He heard there were 13 diamonds

deck of cards?

Why did the robber steal the

◀◀ CHAPTER REVIEW ◀◀

◀◀ Exercise 1 on page 87

A Can these be cut in half to make 2 shapes the same?

1. 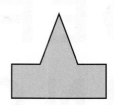   2.    3.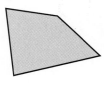

◀◀ Exercise 3 on page 88

B Are these shapes symmetrical?
Write **yes** or **no** for your answer.

1.   2.   3.

◀◀ Exercise 5 on page 92

C Is the dashed line a line of symmetry?

1. 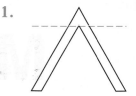   2.   3.

◀◀ Exercise 6 on page 92

D Use a copy of these.
Draw on the line of symmetry.

1.    2. 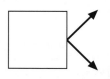   3.

◀◀ Exercise 9 on page 94

E Use a copy of these.
Draw on **all** the lines of symmetry.

1.   2.    3.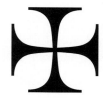

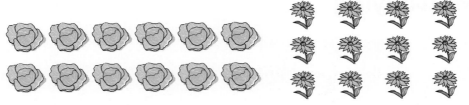

8 Multiplying

Planting ....

Lee planted cabbages.
How many are there?

Jo planted flowers.
How many are there?

Draw a picture for these.
- Sam planted 2 rows of trees.
  There were 5 in each row.
- Sam planted 5 rows of trees.
  There were 3 in each row.

Counting in 2s, 3s, 4s, 5s and 10s

1	2	3	4	5	6	7	8	9	10
11	12	13	14	15	16	17	18	19	20

Every 2nd number is shaded.
We use the table to count in 2s up to 20.
2, 4, 6, 8, 10, 12, 14, 16, 18, 20

Exercise 1

1. Count in 3s up to 30.
   Use the table to help.
   Write down the numbers.

1	2	3	4	5	6	7	8	9	10
11	12	13	14	15	16	17	18	19	20
21	22	23	24	25	26	27	28	29	30

2. Use a copy of the table.
   Shade every 4th number.
   Count in 4s up to 40.
   Write down the numbers.

1	2	3	4	5	6	7	8	9	10
11	12	13	14	15	16	17	18	19	20
21	22	23	24	25	26	27	28	29	30
31	32	33	34	35	36	37	38	39	40

3. Use a copy of the table.
   Shade every 5th number.
   Count in 5s up to 50.
   Write down the numbers.

1	2	3	4	5	6	7	8	9	10
11	12	13	14	15	16	17	18	19	20
21	22	23	24	25	26	27	28	29	30
31	32	33	34	35	36	37	38	39	40
41	42	43	44	45	46	47	48	49	50

4. Use a copy of the table.
Shade every 10th number.
Count in 10s up to 100.
Write down the numbers.

1	2	3	4	5	6	7	8	9	10
11	12	13	14	15	16	17	18	19	20
21	22	23	24	25	26	27	28	29	30
31	32	33	34	35	36	37	38	39	40
41	42	43	44	45	46	47	48	49	50
51	52	53	54	55	56	57	58	59	60
61	62	63	64	65	66	67	68	69	70
71	72	73	74	75	76	77	78	79	80
81	82	83	84	85	86	87	88	89	90
91	92	93	94	95	96	97	98	99	100

Multiplying

How many cakes are there?

We could count the cakes.
1 2 3 4 5 6 7 8 9 10 11 12

We could add up the cakes.
3 + 3 + 3 + 3 = 12

We could multiply.
4 lots of 3.
We write this down as 4 × 3.

To work this out we must know our **multiplication facts**.

2 times table

Learn the facts in this table.

×	1	2	3	4	5	6	7	8	9	10
2	2	4	6	8	10	12	14	16	18	20

Examples   3 × 2 = 6   5 × 2 = 10

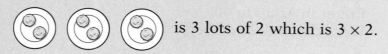 is 3 lots of 2 which is 3 × 2.

 is 5 lots of 2 which is 5 × 2.

Game for 2 players: CARD TIMES

You will need a set of 2s flashcards

To play
- Mix the cards up and put them in a pile.
- One player shows the other each multiplication.
- The other player says the answer and gets 1 point if it is right.

Example Ann and Jack played.

Ann mixed up the cards and picked them up one by one.

The first card she showed Jack was

Jack said "18."

Ann checked on the back that this was right.

Jack got 1 point.

- When all the cards have been shown, swap over.
- The winner is the player who gets the most points.

Exercise 2

Use a copy of this.
Fill in the gaps.
The first one is done.

1. 7×2 is ___7___ lots of ___2___ .

2. 6×2 is _____ lots of _____ . _____

3. 4×2 is _____ lots of _____ . _____

4. 8×2 is _____ lots of _____ . _____

Exercise 3 **A** Write down the answers to these.

1. 4×2	2. 6×2	3. 3×2
4. 8×2	5. 5×2	6. 1×2
7. 9×2	8. 7×2	

B What number goes in the box?

1. ▢ × 2 = 10
2. ▢ × 2 = 4
3. ▢ × 2 = 6
4. ▢ × 2 = 16
5. ▢ × 2 = 18
6. ▢ × 2 = 12
7. ▢ × 2 = 14
8. ▢ × 2 = 2
9. ▢ × 2 = 20

3 times table

Learn the facts in this table.

×	1	2	3	4	5	6	7	8	9	10
3	3	6	9	12	15	18	21	24	27	30

Examples $4 \times 3 = 12$ $6 \times 3 = 18$

 is 4 lots of 3 which is 4×3.

 is 6 lots of 3 which is 6×3.

Exercise 4

Use a copy of this.
Fill in the gaps.
The first one is done.

1. 2×3 is __2__ lots of __3__ .

2. 3×3 is ____ lots of ____ .

3. 5×3 is ____ lots of ____ .

4. 7×3 is ____ lots of ____ .

Game   Play **CARD TIMES** on page **101** with a set of 3s flashcards.

Exercise 5   **A**   Write down the answers to these.

1. 1×3 2. 4×3 3. 3×3
4. 6×3 5. 5×3 6. 8×3
7. 10×3 8. 9×3

B   What goes in the box?

1. $\square \times 3 = 9$ 2. $\square \times 3 = 12$ 3. $\square \times 3 = 6$
4. $\square \times 3 = 3$ 5. $\square \times 3 = 18$ 6. $\square \times 3 = 24$
7. $\square \times 3 = 30$ 8. $\square \times 3 = 21$

4 times table

Learn the facts in this table.

×	1	2	3	4	5	6	7	8	9	10
4	4	8	12	16	20	24	28	32	36	40

Examples $6 \times 4 = 24$ $7 \times 4 = 28$

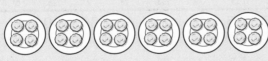

is 6 lots of 4 which is 6×4.

is 7 lots of 4 which is 7×4.

Exercise 6   Use a copy of this.
Fill in the gaps.
The first one is done.

1. 5×4 is __5__ lots of __4__ .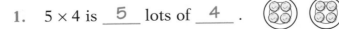

2. 3×4 is _____ lots of _____ .

3. 8×4 is _____ lots of _____ .

4. 10×4 is _____ lots of _____ .

Exercise 7   **A**   Write down the answers to these.

1. 2×4
2. 4×4
3. 3×4
4. 6×4
5. 8×4
6. 5×4
7. 7×4
8. 10×4
9. 9×4

B   What number goes in the box?

1. $\boxed{} \times 4 = 8$
2. $\boxed{} \times 4 = 20$
3. $\boxed{} \times 4 = 32$
4. $\boxed{} \times 4 = 4$
5. $\boxed{} \times 4 = 40$
6. $\boxed{} \times 4 = 16$
7. $\boxed{} \times 4 = 24$
8. $\boxed{} \times 4 = 28$

5 times table

Learn the facts in this table.

$\times$	1	2	3	4	5	6	7	8	9	10
5	5	10	15	20	25	30	35	40	45	50

Examples $6 \times 5 = 30$ $8 \times 5 = 40$ $5 \times 5 = 25$ $9 \times 5 = 45$

Exercise 8   **A**   Write down the answers to these.

1. 2×5
2. 4×5
3. 7×5
4. 3×5
5. 8×5
6. 10×5
7. 6×5
8. 1×5
9. 9×5

B   What number goes in the box?

1. $\boxed{} \times 5 = 5$
2. $\boxed{} \times 5 = 15$
3. $\boxed{} \times 5 = 30$
4. $\boxed{} \times 5 = 20$
5. $\boxed{} \times 5 = 35$
6. $\boxed{} \times 5 = 10$
7. $\boxed{} \times 5 = 40$
8. $\boxed{} \times 5 = 50$

10 times table

Learn the facts on this table.

×	1	2	3	4	5	6	7	8	9	10
10	10	20	30	40	50	60	70	80	90	100

Examples $6 \times 10 = 60$ $9 \times 10 = 90$ $4 \times 10 = 40$ $7 \times 10 = 70$

Game

Play **CARD TIMES** on page 101 with a set of 10s flashcards.

Exercise 9   **A**   Write down the answers to these.

1. 2×10
2. 5×10
3. 3×10
4. 7×10
5. 1×10
6. 8×10
7. 9×10
8. 6×10
9. 10×10

B   What number goes in the box?

1. $\square \times 10 = 60$
2. $\square \times 10 = 40$
3. $\square \times 10 = 10$
4. $\square \times 10 = 90$
5. $\square \times 10 = 70$
6. $\square \times 10 = 20$
7. $\square \times 10 = 80$
8. $\square \times 10 = 100$

Exercise 10   Write down the answers to these.

1. 4×3
2. 6×2
3. 5×3
4. 2×4
5. 5×10
6. 7×2
7. 7×3
8. 5×5
9. 8×2
10. 6×3
11. 7×10
12. 7×5
13. 5×4
14. 7×4
15. 8×10
16. 9×4
17. 8×3
18. 9×3
19. 8×4
20. 6×4

Exercise 11   Use a copy of these.
Fill in the missing numbers.

1.

×	3	4	5
2			
3			
4			

2.

×	9	7	10
2			
4			
5			

Homework/Review 1

A 1. Count in 3s up to 30. Write down the numbers.
2. Count in 5s up to 50. Write down the numbers.
3. Count in 4s up to 40. Write down the numbers.
4. Count in 10s up to 100. Write down the numbers.

B What number goes in the box?

1. $3 \times \square = 12$ 2. $\square \times 5 = 20$ 3. $9 \times \square = 45$
4. $\square \times 5 = 35$ 5. $10 \times \square = 40$ 6. $\square \times 3 = 21$
7. $8 \times 4 = \square$ 8. $9 \times 3 = \square$ 9. $10 \times \square = 10$
10. $7 \times \square = 28$ 11. $\square \times 3 = 18$ 12. $8 \times 3 = \square$
13. $\square \times 5 = 50$ 14. $6 \times 5 = \square$ 15. $4 \times \square = 16$
16. $\square \times 5 = 15$ 17. $\square \times 4 = 24$

C **Where do cows go for a night out?**
Use a copy of the box.

H $3 \times 2 = 6$
S 8×3
E 7×5
T 9×5
I 9×4
V 8×4
M 9×3
O 7×4

45	28		45	H / 6	35	
27	28	28	32	36	35	24

More multiplying

Investigation

● Copy these. Write down the answers.

$2 \times 4 =$ $5 \times 4 =$ $3 \times 10 =$ $3 \times 4 =$
$4 \times 2 =$ $4 \times 5 =$ $10 \times 3 =$ $4 \times 3 =$

Copy this sentence. Fill in the gap with **does** or **does not**.

When we multiply two numbers it _____ matter what order they are in.

● 0 lots of 5 is the same as 0×5.
What do you think 0 lots of 5 is equal to?
Copy these. Write down the answers.

$0 \times 5 =$	$0 \times 4 =$	$0 \times 2 =$
$0 \times 3 =$	$0 \times 10 =$	$0 \times 1 =$

Copy this sentence. Finish it.
When we multiply by 0 the answer is always _____ .

Exercise 12   Write down the answers to these.

1. 6×2	2. 3×5	3. 2×9
4. 4×2	5. 4×3	6. 0×3
7. 0×10	8. 5×10	9. 4×6
10. 5×7	11. 3×8	12. 5×9
13. 10×6	14. 4×9	15. 5×8
16. 3×9	17. 5×6	18. 3×6
19. 3×7	20. 4×7	21. 4×8
22. 10×9	23. 8×0	

Exercise 13   Use a copy of these.
Fill in the missing numbers.

1.

×	3	4	5
6			
9			
8			

2.

×		4	10
7	21		
		36	
			50

Exercise 14   ☐ × ☐ = 20

Find ways to fill in the boxes.
Don't use numbers bigger than 10.

Exercise 15   Use a copy of this.
Find numbers to go in the green squares.
Try to find more than one way.

×		
	12	
		20

Example   There are 5 cakes on each plate.
How many would there be on 6 plates?

Answer   There are 6 lots of 5.
6 × 5 = 30

Exercise 16   **A**   Matt went to the bakers.

1.   There were 7 plates of cakes.
Each plate had 4 cakes on it.
How many cakes were there altogether?

2.   There were 8 plates of pies.
Each plate had 5 pies on it.
How many pies were there altogether?

3.   There were 3 plates of rum balls.
Each plate had 9 rum balls on it.
How many rum balls were there altogether?

B   1.   Matt bought 6 mugs for his mother.
How much did these cost?

2.   Matt bought 5 mugs for his sister.
How much did these cost?

3.   Matt bought 7 mugs for his friend.
How much did these cost?

£4.00 each

C

SUCKERS
5p each

GREEN BALLS
4p each

PLANES
10p each

1.   Matt bought 5 suckers.
How much did this cost?

2.   Matt bought 9 green balls.
How much did this cost?

3.   Matt bought 8 planes.
How much did this cost?

Game for 2 players: MULTIPLYING DICE

You will need   2 dice
12 green counters
12 red counters
this board

4	5	4	24	6	9	16	8
24	1	25	8	15	20	3	6
16	12	10	2	20	10	12	1
6	18	12	25	6	15	4	18
8	5	30	3	12	2	30	24

To play
- Take turns to roll two dice.
- Multiply the two numbers together.
- Put a counter on the answer.
  You cannot have more than one counter on any square.
- If you roll two sixes, you can put your counter on any square.
- The winner is the first person to get 3 counters in a line.

Examples

6	9	16	8
●	●	●	6
20	10	12	1
6	15	4	18

or

●	9	16	8
●	20	3	6
●	10	12	1
6	15	4	18

or

6	9	16	8
15	20	●	6
20	●	12	1
●	15	4	18

or

●	9	16	8
15	●	3	6
20	10	●	1
6	15	4	18

Homework/Review 2

A   Use a copy of these.
Fill in the missing numbers.

1.

×	2	4	10
3			
8			
5			

2.

×	5	3	
6			24
		21	
9			

B   Why are horses always badly dressed?

Use a copy of the box.

E	$3 \times 6 = 18$
O	10×5
A	4×4
R	4×3
U	3×7
T	4×5
B	5×6
C	10×7
H	4×9
Y	5×9
N	4×7
W	3×9
K	5×8
S	3×8

```
            E                    E              E
 ── ── ── ── ── ── ──     ── ── ── ──
 30 18 70 16 21 24 18     20 36 18 45

       E                    E
 ── ── ── ──     ── ── ── ── ──
 27 18 16 12     24 36 50 18 24


 ── ── ──     ── ── ──     ── ── ── ── ──
 30 21 20     28 50 20     24 50 70 40 24
```

C   **1.**   Jen bought 6 tickets.
How much did these cost?

2.   Jon bought 8 tickets.
How much did these cost?

3.   Maya and her friends bought 7 lunches.
How much did these cost?

4.   The Bar family bought 8 lunches.
How much did these cost?

Skating

Tickets: £4.00
Lunch: £3.00

◀◀ CHAPTER REVIEW ◀◀

◀◀
Exercise 1
on page 99

A 1. Count in 2s up to 18. Write down the numbers.
   2. Count in 3s up to 21. Write down the numbers.
   3. Count in 5s up to 45. Write down the numbers.
   4. Count in 4s up to 40. Write down the numbers.

◀◀
Exercise 3
on page 101

B What number goes in the box?

1. $5 \times 2 = \square$ 2. $4 \times 2 = \square$ 3. $9 \times 2 = \square$
4. $\square \times 2 = 20$ 5. $\square \times 2 = 16$ 6. $\square \times 2 = 14$

◀◀
Exercise 5
on page 103

C What number goes in the box?

1. $4 \times 3 = \square$ 2. $8 \times 3 = \square$ 3. $9 \times 3 = \square$
4. $\square \times 3 = 30$ 5. $\square \times 3 = 18$ 6. $\square \times 3 = 21$

◀◀
Exercise 7
on page 104

D What number goes in the box?

1. $4 \times 4 = \square$ 2. $6 \times 4 = \square$ 3. $5 \times 4 = \square$
4. $\square \times 4 = 36$ 5. $\square \times 4 = 28$ 6. $\square \times 4 = 32$

◀◀
Exercise 8
on page 104

E What number goes in the box?

1. $3 \times 5 = \square$ 2. $5 \times 5 = \square$ 3. $7 \times 5 = \square$
4. $\square \times 5 = 30$ 5. $\square \times 5 = 45$ 6. $\square \times 5 = 40$

◀◀
Exercise 9
on page 105

F What number goes in the box?

1. $1 \times 10 = \square$ 2. $4 \times 10 = \square$ 3. $6 \times 10 = \square$
4. $\square \times 10 = 80$ 5. $\square \times 10 = 90$ 6. $\square \times 10 = 100$

◀◀
Exercise 12
on page 107

G Write down the answers to these.

1. 4×4 2. 3×7 3. 8×4 4. 5×9
5. 8×3 6. 9×4 7. 4×7 8. 6×0

◀◀
Exercise 13
on page 107

H Use a copy of these.
Fill in the missing numbers.

1.

×	8	7	4
2			
5			
10			

2.

×	9	6	5
3			
5			
4			

3.

×	10	9	8
5			
		27	
			32

Clocks...

Some clocks are shown.
Make up a clock of your own.
Draw a picture of it.

Measuring time

We measure time in **years**, **months**, **weeks**, **days**, **hours**, **minutes** and **seconds**.

Do we measure time any other way?

Try to answer these.
What is a leap year?
How many days are in a year?
How many months are in a year?
How many weeks are in a year?
How many days are in a week?
How many hours are in a day?
How many minutes are in an hour?
How many seconds are in a minute?

The months in order are:

January, February, March, April, May, June, July, August, September, October, November, December.

Some have 30 days.
Some have 31 days.
February has 28 days but in a leap year it has 29 days.

To help you remember
Make two fists.
All the bumps have 31 days.

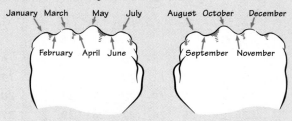

Exercise 1   How many days are in these?

1. March   2. November 3. July   4. December
5. February   6. August   7. January   8. September

These are ways of writing the date.

	day	month	year
15th August 1998 15/8/98	15	08	98

Exercise 2   **A** Write these dates in two other ways.

The first is done for you.

1. 17th May 1999   17/5/99 and | 17 | 05 | 99 |

2. 24th July 1998

3. 4th September 1964

4. 5/3/72

5. | 16 | 01 | 94 |

6. | 03 | 10 | 54 |

B   Which month is given by these dates?

1.

2.

3.

We use **calendars** to tell us the month, day and date.

August

Sun	Mon	Tues	Wed	Thurs	Fri	Sat
						1
2	3	4	5	6	7	8
9	10	11	12	13	14	15
16	17	18	19	20	21	22
23	24	25	26	27	28	29
30	31					

September

Sun	Mon	Tues	Wed	Thurs	Fri	Sat
		1	2	3	4	5
6	7	8	9	10	11	12
13	14	15	16	17	18	19
20	21	22	23	24	25	26
27	28	29	30			

Example   August the 16th is a Sunday.

Exercise 3

1. What day was August the 20th?
2. What day was September the 11th?
3. What day was August the 25th?
4. What day was September the 26th?
5. What day was September the 13th?
6. What day was August the 30th?

the **minute** hand

the **hour** hand

On the hour, the minute hand points straight up.

This clock says 3 o'clock.

Exercise 4   What is the time?

1.

2.

3.

4.

5.

6.

7.

Examples

This clock says
half past one.

This clock says
quarter past ten.

This clock says
quarter to six.

Exercise 5   What is the time?

1.

2.

3.

4.

5.

6.

7.

8.

We read the minute hand like this.

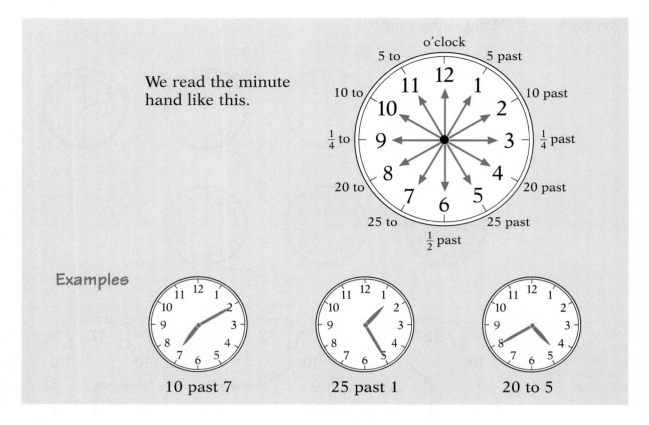

Examples

10 past 7   25 past 1   20 to 5

Exercise 6   What is the time?

1.

2.

3.

4.

5.

6.

7.

8.

9.

10.

11.

12.

Exercise 7   Use a copy of these.

Put hands on the clock to show the time.

1.

20 past 4

2.

10 past 8

3.

5 to 10

4.

20 to 11

5.

quarter to 3

6.

25 past 1

7.

10 to 12

8.

25 to 6

Homework/Review 1

A How many days are in these?

   1. April   2. June   3. May   4. October

B Write the date you were born in 3 ways.

C What day were these?

   1. November 11th

   2. November 23rd

   3. November 8th

   4. November 28th

   5. November 5th

November

Sun	Mon	Tues	Wed	Thurs	Fri	Sat
1	2	3	4	5	6	7
8	9	10	11	12	13	14
15	16	17	18	19	20	21
22	23	24	25	26	27	28
29	30					

D **Why can't you keep a clock in jail?**

Use a copy of this box.

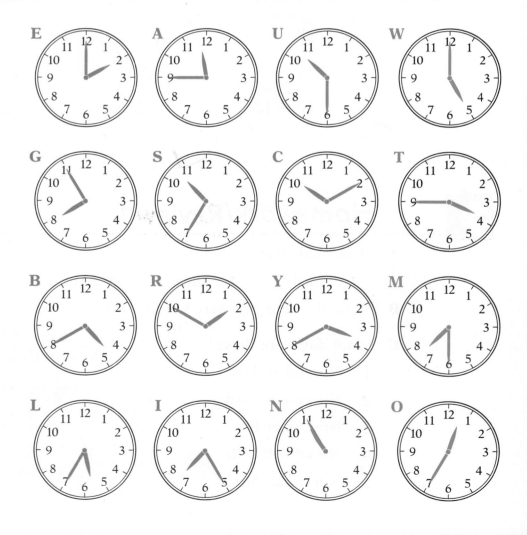

	E					E	
20 to 5	2 o'clock	10 past 10	$\frac{1}{4}$ to 12	5 o'clock	25 to 11	2 o'clock	

		E				
$\frac{1}{4}$ to 4	25 past 7	$\frac{1}{2}$ past 7	2 o'clock		25 past 7	25 to 11

$\frac{1}{4}$ to 12	25 to 6	$\frac{1}{2}$ past 10	$\frac{1}{4}$ to 12	20 to 4	25 to 11

10 to 2	$\frac{1}{2}$ past 10	5 to 11	5 to 11	25 past 7	5 to 11	5 to 8	25 to 1	5 o'clock	$\frac{1}{4}$ to 4

Digital time

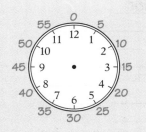

The minutes **past** each hour are shown in green.

A **digital clock** shows the minutes *past* each hour.

Examples

 25 to 4 is shown as 3:35.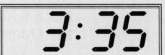

 10 to 4 is shown as 3:50.

Exercise 8

A  B   P

Q

C   D   R

S

E   F   T

U

What letter goes in the gap?
The first one is done.

1. A matches with ___S___. 2. B matches with _____.
3. C matches with _____. 4. D matches with _____.
5. E matches with _____. 6. F matches with _____.

Exercise 9

What digital time goes in the gap?
The first one is done.

1. 10 to 9 is the same as __8:50__ .
2. 20 past 7 is the same as _____ .
3. Half past 9 is the same as _____ .
4. 25 past 3 is the same as _____ .
5. Quarter past 12 is the same as _____ .
6. 10 to 5 is the same as _____ .
7. 20 to 7 is the same as _____ .
8. 5 to 8 is the same as _____ .
9. 25 to 11 is the same as _____ .
10. Quarter to 10 is the same as _____ .
11. 5 to 1 is the same as _____ .
12. Quarter to 1 is the same as _____ .

We use a **stop watch** to measure seconds.
We can also measure seconds with watches that have a
second hand.

Task

You will need a stop watch or a watch with a second hand
Ask your teacher how to use the stop watch.

A Estimate how long it would take you to do these things.
Do them. Have someone time you.

> write your name 5 times
> count back from 10 to 1
> say the date you were born 10 times

B Start the stop watch. Close your eyes.
Stop it when you think 1 minute is up.
How long was it really? Do this lots of times. Did you get better?

a.m. and p.m. time

The hour hand goes round twice each day.

Example There is 8 o'clock in the morning and 8 o'clock at night.

Time in the morning is a.m. time.
Time in the afternoon and at night is p.m. time.

Example Tom got up at 8 a.m.
Menna went to bed at 9:30 p.m.

Exercise 10 Write these times using a.m. or p.m.

1. 9 o'clock in the morning
2. 3 o'clock in the afternoon
3. 7 o'clock at night
4. 4 o'clock in the morning
5. 4 o'clock in the afternoon
6. 7:15 in the morning
7. 6:25 at night
8. 11:35 at night
9. 12:20 in the morning
10. 5:05 in the morning
11. 2:10 in the afternoon
12. 4:45 in the afternoon

Example The time on this sign is 8 p.m.

DANCE *at the hall*
8 o'clock Wednesday night

Exercise 11 Are the times on these a.m. or p.m. times?

1. SCHOOL TRIP
   to beach
   bus leaves 10 o'clock

2. EARLY MORNING
   First train
   leaves
   6 o'clock

3. *CARDIFF*
   v
   WREXHAM
   kick off
   2 o'clock

4. Shop Late
   TONIGHT
   open till
   9 o'clock

5. HAIR CUTS
   Open
   Sat morning
   9–12

Exercise 12 Write down what you did yesterday at these times.

1. 8 a.m.
2. 6:30 p.m.
3. 3 a.m.
4. 2:20 p.m.
5. 5:10 p.m.
6. 12:45 p.m.

Homework/Review 2

A Write these times using a.m. or p.m.

1. 7 o'clock in the morning
2. 5 o'clock in the afternoon
3. 9 o'clock at night   4. 5:20 in the morning
5. 11:15 at night   6. 3:35 in the afternoon

B Are the times on these a.m. or p.m. times?

1.

2.

C **When does a jumper jump highest?**

Use a copy of this box.

E   20 past 4
I   half past 2
R   25 past 11
N   20 to 7
P   5 to 8
Y   25 to 9
L   quarter to 1
A   10 to 5

2:30	6:40		4:50
		E	
12:45	4:20	4:50	7:55
		E	
8:35	4:20	4:50	11:25

D   12:30 p.m. 8:20 a.m. 4:30 p.m. 5:45 p.m. 7:15 a.m. 8:45 p.m.

Which time from the box goes in the gap?

1. Maria went to bed at _____ .

2. Maria went to school at _____ .

3. Maria ate tea at _____ .

4. Maria ate lunch at _____ .

5. Maria went to netball at _____ .

6. Maria got up at _____ .

◀◀ CHAPTER REVIEW ◀◀

Exercise 1
on page 113

A How many days are in these?

1. November 2. July 3. February 4. August
5. May 6. October 7. January 8. April

Exercise 2
on page 113

B What is the month given by the dates on these?

1.
2.
3.

Exercise 3
on page 114

C What day were these?

1. April 20th
2. April 30th
3. April 11th
4. April 26th

		April				
Sun	Mon	Tues	Wed	Thurs	Fri	Sat
			1	2	3	4
5	6	7	8	9	10	11
12	13	14	15	16	17	18
19	20	21	22	23	24	25
26	27	28	29	30		

Exercise 4
on page 115

D What is the time?

1.
2.
3.
4.

Exercise 5
on page 115

E What is the time?

1.
2.
3.
4.

◄◄

Exercise 6
on page 116

F What is the time?

1.

2.

3.

4.

◄◄

Exercise 7
on page 117

G Use a copy of these.

Put the hands on the clock to show the time.

1.

25 past 7

2.
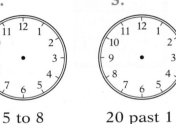
5 to 8

3.
20 past 1

4.

25 to 11

◄◄

Exercise 9
on page 120

H What digital time goes in the gap?

The first one is done.

1. 20 past 8 is the same as ___8:20___ .

2. 25 to 10 is the same as _____ .

3. 10 to 1 is the same as _____ .

4. Quarter to 9 is the same as _____ .

◄◄

Exercise 10
on page 121

I Write these times using a.m. or p.m.

1. 7 o'clock in the morning
2. 4 o'clock in the afternoon
3. 5:20 in the evening
4. 2:20 in the afternoon

◄◄

Exercise 11
on page 121

J Are the times on these a.m. or p.m. times?

1.
DISCO
Wednesday 4th
8 o'clock

2.
SPORTS DAY
this Saturday
11 o'clock

Quick Test 3

Beth worked for 'Pet Minders'.

A There was a sign outside Beth's work.

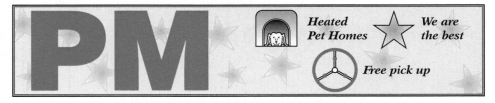

1. Is the letter P symmetrical?
2. Is the letter M symmetrical?

B The sign also had these pictures on it.

Use a copy of these.

Draw on **all** the lines of symmetry.

1.  2.  3.

C

1. Val left her bird at Pet Minders for 8 nights.
   How much did this cost?

2. Gary left his small dog for 7 nights.
   How much did this cost?

3. Karen left her big dog for 9 nights.
   How much did this cost?

4. Sam left his cat for 8 nights.
   How much did this cost?

D Gary left his dog on this date.
What is the month given by this date?

8/9/98

E The dogs were fed at these times.
Write down what these times are.

1.    2.

F These are the other feeding times.

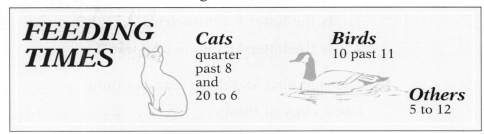

FEEDING TIMES   **Cats** quarter past 8 and 20 to 6   **Birds** 10 past 11   **Others** 5 to 12

What digital time goes in the gap?
The first one is done.

1. quarter past 8 is the same as ___8:15___ .

2. 20 to 6 is the same as _____ .

3. 10 past 11 is the same as _____ .

4. 5 to 12 is the same as _____ .

G Are the times on these signs a.m. or p.m. times?

1. **TAKE DOGS FOR A RUN**   11:45

2.
Turn lights out   9:30

10 Collecting and Sorting Data

Eating out...

Sue asked her friends which of these they liked best.

Glyn asked his friends which drink they liked best when they ate out.

What could you ask your friends about eating out?

Collection sheets

Pam asked her friends what drink they liked best.

Jan likes cola	Anna likes cola	Bob likes water
Paul likes cola	Aled likes milk	David likes water
Penny likes milk	Liz likes milk	Zenta likes cola

Pam could use one of these as a **collection sheet**.

Drink	How many	Total
cola	XXXX	4
milk	XXX	3
water	XX	2

Drink		
cola	milk	water
IIII	III	II
4	3	2

Make your own collection sheet for Pam's question.

Example Karen rolled these numbers in a game.

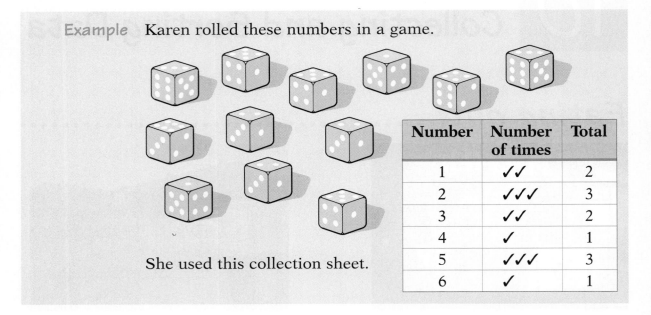

Number	Number of times	Total
1	✓✓	2
2	✓✓✓	3
3	✓✓	2
4	✓	1
5	✓✓✓	3
6	✓	1

She used this collection sheet.

Exercise 1

1. Brenda rolled these numbers in a game.

   Use a copy of her collection sheet.

   Finish filling it in.

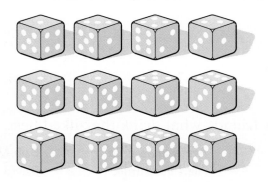

Number rolled	Number of times	Total
1	✗	
2		
3		
4		
5		
6		

2. Deri asked his friends what pets they had.

   Use a copy of his collection sheet.

   Finish filling it in.

Pet	Number	Total
cat		
dog	✓	
rabbit		
hamster		

   dog cat cat rabbit hamster
   cat cat dog hamster rabbit

3. Nina asked her friends what colour they liked best.

Use a copy of her collection sheet.

Finish filling it in.

Colour	Number	Total
red	I	
blue		
green		
pink		
yellow		
purple		

red	blue	red	blue
green	purple	yellow	pink
pink	red	blue	red
pink	purple	blue	pink

4. Mike asked his friends what fruit they had for lunch.

Use a copy of his collection sheet.

Finish filling it in.

Fruit		
apple	orange	banana
✓		
Total:	Total:	Total:

Example   Fay asked her friends how they came to school.

She used this collection sheet.

Way	How many	Total
walk	IIII	4
bus	IIIIIIIIIIIIIIIIIIIIII	22
bike	IIIIIIII	8
train	I	1

To make the marks easy to count, we put them in lots of 5.

ШH is 5.

ШH ШH is 10.

This is called a **tally** chart.

Way	Tally	Total
walk	IIII	4
bus	ШH ШH ШH ШH II	22
bike	ШH III	8
train	I	1

Exercise 2   What totals are shown by these?

1. ШH
2. ШH ШH
3. ШH ШH ШH
4. ШH II
5. ШH ШH III
6. ШH ШH IIII
7. ШH IIII
8. ШH ШH ШH I
9. ШH ШH ШH ШH II

Exercise 3

1. Ted asked his friends which coins they had.

   Use a copy of this tally chart.

   Fill it in .

Coin	Tally	Total
£1		
50 p		
20 p		
10 p		
5 p		

   £1   20p   £1   5p   50p
      10p   £1 £1   £1   20p
        £1 50p £1   50p   50p
   £1   50p 50p 20p   10p

2. Lucy asked her friends what they got from the tuck shop.

   Use a copy of this tally chart.

   Fill it in.

Food	Tally	Total
crisps		
fruit		
roll		
bun		

   crisps   bun   roll crisps   bun
      fruit bun   roll   crisps roll
   crisps   bun roll crisps   roll
   crisps fruit   bun crisps bun
   roll crisps crisps   roll   bun

3. Sudi asked her friends what ice-cream they liked best.

   Use a copy of this tally chart.

   Fill it in.

Ice-cream	Chocolate	Vanilla	Strawberry	Lime	Coffee
Tally					
Total					

   lime   strawberry chocolate strawberry   chocolate
   vanilla vanilla chocolate chocolate   chocolate
   lime vanilla   chocolate lime   vanilla chocolate
   strawberry chocolate   coffee lime   chocolate
   vanilla chocolate strawberry chocolate chocolate
   vanilla vanilla lime vanilla   chocolate strawberry
   chocolate chocolate   chocolate vanilla   strawberry

Task 1

Choose **one** of these questions to ask your friends.

What show on TV do you like best?
What pet do you like best?
What colour are your eyes?
What sport do you like best?

Make up a collection sheet for your question.
Just have 4 or 5 things for your friends to
choose from.
Ask your friends the question.
Put the answers on the collection sheet.

Homework/Review 1

A Mary asked her friends what type
of meal they liked best.
Use a copy of her collection sheet.
Finish filling it in.

Meal	Number	Total
lamb	✓	
beef		
chicken		
fish		

lamb   fish   fish   chicken
   beef   chicken   chicken
beef   lamb   chicken
   fish   fish   fish

B What totals are shown by these?

1. 卌
2. 卌 II
3. 卌 卌 I
4. 卌 卌 卌
5. 卌 卌 III
6. 卌 卌 卌 III

C Will asked his friends which number
out of 1, 2, 3, 4 and 5 they liked best.
Use a copy of this tally chart.
Fill it in.

Number liked best	Tally	Total
1		
2		
3		
4		
5		

```
1   2   4   1   3   5   1
5   3   5   1   5   5   1
3   4   5   5   3   1   4
3   5   1   2   4   5   5
5   1   2   5   5   3   5
3   5   1   3   5   2   5
```

Sorting

1 3 15 8 7 4 17 11
19 5 14 10 6 9 8 13

We can sort these numbers into odd numbers and even numbers.

odd: 1   3   15 7   17 11 19 5   9   13
even: 8   4   14 10 6   8

There are 10 odd numbers
and 6 even numbers.

odd	10
even	6

We can also sort them into green numbers and black numbers.

green:15 17 5   14 6   8   13
black: 1   3   8   7   4   11 19 10 9

There are 7 green numbers
and 9 black numbers.

blue	7
black	9

Exercise 4

Use a copy of the tables.

Fill them in.

1.

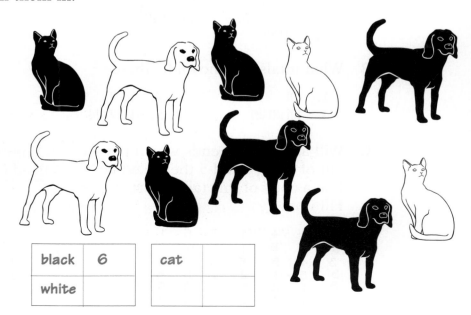

black	6
white	

cat	

2.   7   **8**   1   **5**   2   6   **9**   **4**   3

odd	

small	

3.

shoes	

black	

4.   Kay has blue eyes and blonde hair.
Cath has brown eyes and brown hair.
Ros has blue eyes and brown hair.
Carol has blue eyes and brown hair.

blue eyes	

5.   Roger has been in hospital and had stitches.
John has never been in hospital but has had stitches.
Lee has been in hospital but has never had stitches.
Gerard has been in hospital but has never had stitches.
Glyn has never been in hospital and has never had stitches.
Owen has never been in hospital and has never had stitches.

been in hospital	

Two-way tables

We can use a **two-way table** to sort things in two ways.

Ben   Anna   Gwen   Vijay   Nia   Liz   Tim   Lela   Pam   Ian

In this picture we have boys and girls.
Some have a coat and some don't.
4 girls are wearing coats.
2 girls are not wearing coats.
1 boy is wearing a coat.
3 boys are not wearing coats.

4	2	girls
1	3	boys

wearing coat   not wearing coat

This is a two-way table.

Exercise 5   **A**   3 7 4 1 2 8 5 6

1. How many of these numbers are odd and black?

2. How many are odd and green?

3. How many are even and black?

4. How many are even and green?

5. Use a copy of this two-way table.
   Fill it in.

		odd
		even

black   green

B Use a copy of this two-way table.
Fill it in.

		round
		square

green   not green

11 Angles, Slides and Turns

At the fun park...

These rides at the fun park **turn** people in some way.

What other rides turn people?

Right angles

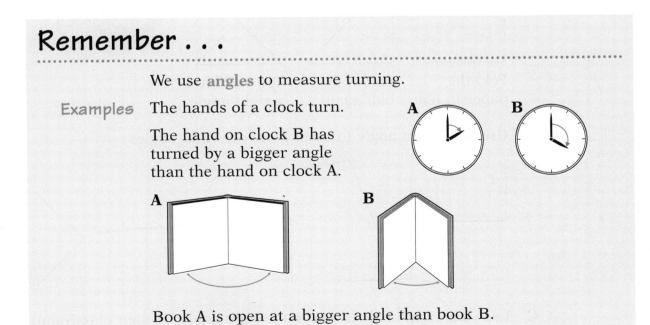

Remember . . .

We use angles to measure turning.

Examples The hands of a clock turn.

The hand on clock B has turned by a bigger angle than the hand on clock A.

A   B

A   B

Book A is open at a bigger angle than book B.

This is a **right angle**.

We show it is a right angle like this.

Lots of things have right angles.

Examples The corners of this page are right angles.

A door has 4 right angles.

Task 1

You will need a sheet of square paper

A

Fold the paper in half.　Fold it in half again.　You will have a right angle.

B Use **your** right angle to see if these are right angles.

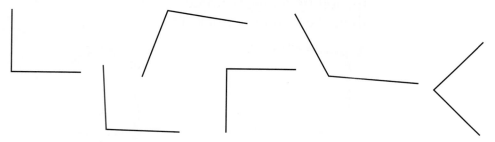

C Use your right angle to find some right angles in your classroom.

Exercise 1   Which of these have right angles?

Exercise 2   Write down the 5 letters which are beside right angles.

Make a word from these letters.

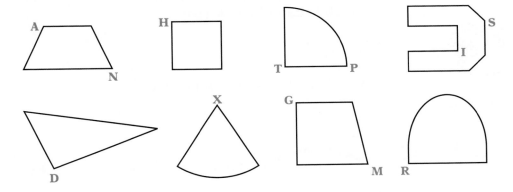

Exercise 3   How many right angles do these have?

1.

2.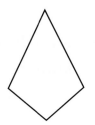

3.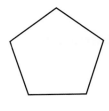

4.

5.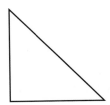

6.

Puzzle

How many right angles can you find?

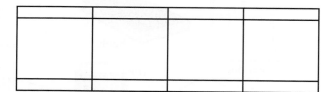

Clockwise and anticlockwise

The way the hands move around a clock is called **clockwise**.

The other way is **anticlockwise**.

Example

This arrow is pointing clockwise.

This arrow is pointing anticlockwise.

Exercise 4

1. Write down the letters of the arrows pointing clockwise.

2. Write down the letters of the arrows pointing anticlockwise.

A ⟩   B ⌢   C (D ⟩

E ⌣   F ( )   G ⌢   H ⟍

I ⟨   J ⌢   K (

Game for 2 players: RAINBOW

You will need   a cube with A1, A2, A3, C1, C2, C3
the board below
a counter for each player

To play
- Put your counter on one of the start squares.
- Take turns to toss the cube.
- Move the way the cube tells you.
  A stands for anticlockwise. C stands for clockwise.
  A1 means move 1 square anticlockwise.
  A2 means move 2 squares anticlockwise.
  C3 means move 3 squares clockwise.
- The winner is the first player to reach a pot of gold.
- You must get the exact number to reach the pot of gold.

Example   If you toss A2 and you need A1 to reach the pot, you can't move.

Exercise 5

1 right angle anticlockwise	1 right angle clockwise
2 right angles anticlockwise	2 right angles clockwise
3 right angles anticlockwise	3 right angles clockwise

What angle has the black shape been turned by?
Choose from the box.

1.

2.

3.

4.

5.

Example   Draw this arrow after it has been turned
1 right angle clockwise.

Answer   We turn the arrow this way

The answer is   ⟶

Exercise 6   Draw this arrow after it has been turned by these.

1.   2 right angles clockwise

2.   1 right angle anticlockwise

3.   2 right angles anticlockwise

4.   3 right angles clockwise

5.   3 right angles anticlockwise

6.   4 right angles clockwise

7.   4 right angles anticlockwise

Exercise 7

A space buggy is moving around on Mars.
The space buggy begins in the green square.
Use a copy of this to find out where it ends.

						L					
						Q		R		A	
	B	V					N				U
	W					T			C		
		S				Y	D			M	
		F			P	E		O			Z
L		K		J		X	H			I	
	G			N							

The first 3 moves have been done.

Example   The space buggy has turned 1 right angle clockwise.

It moves 2 squares forward
turns 1 right angle clockwise
moves 4 squares forward
turns 1 right angle anticlockwise
moves 3 squares forward
turns 2 right angles anticlockwise
moves 4 squares forward
turns 3 right angles clockwise
moves 2 squares forward
turns 1 right angle clockwise
moves 1 square forward
turns 2 right angles clockwise
moves 5 squares forward.

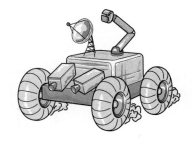

Exercise 8

Make up your own moves for the space buggy.
Give them to a friend to work out.

Homework/Review 1

A Write down the letters that are beside right angles.

Make a word from these letters.

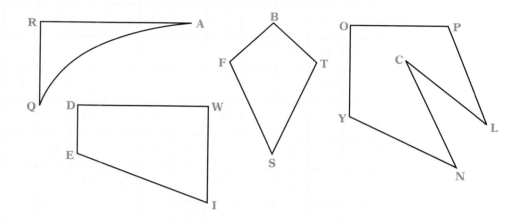

B Is the pole turning clockwise or anticlockwise?

1.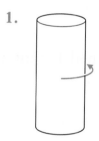

2.

3.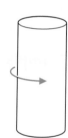

C 1. ⟶ Draw this arrow after it has been turned 1 right angle clockwise.

2. ↑ Draw this arrow after it has been turned 3 right angles anticlockwise.

3. ↓ Draw this arrow after it has been turned 2 right angles clockwise.

4. ⟵ Draw this arrow after it has been turned 4 right angles anticlockwise.

5. ↑ Draw this arrow after it has been turned 3 right angles clockwise.

Turns and slides

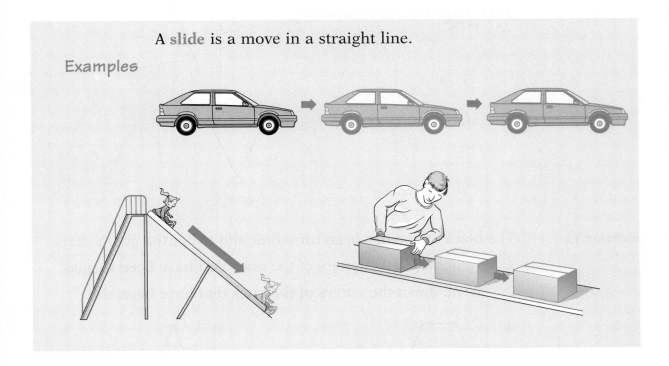

A **slide** is a move in a straight line.

Examples

Exercise 9

1. Which of these are **turns**?

2. Which are **slides**?

A an egg being dropped

B a car going round a corner

C the big hand on a clock

D a train moving

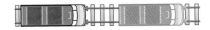

E a boy on a swing

Examples

This shape has been **turned**.

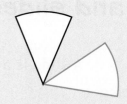

This shape has been **slid**.

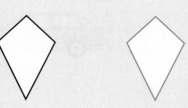

Exercise 10   The black shape has been turned or slid to get the green shape.

1.   Write down the letters of the ones that have been turned.

2.   Write down the letters of the ones that have been slid.

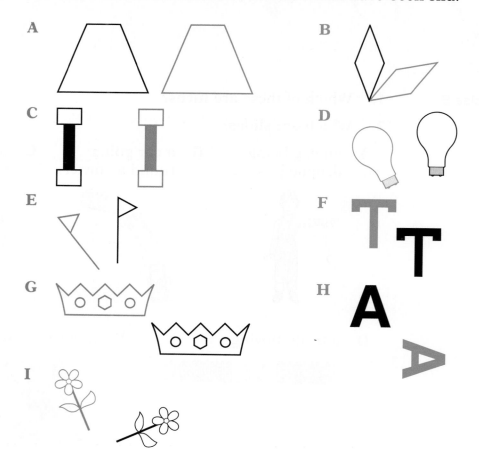

Exercise 11   The pattern on the right has been made using the shape on
the left.

   1.   Which patterns were made by sliding the shape?

   2.   Which pattern was made by turning the shape?

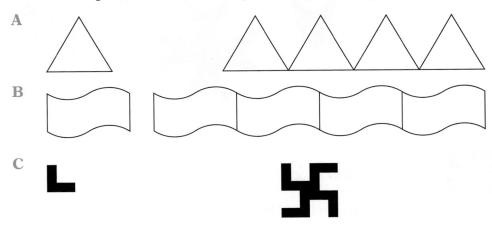

Homework/Review 2

  A Use a copy of the box.

Which of these are turns and which are slides?

Put a line from the picture to the word.

The first one is done.

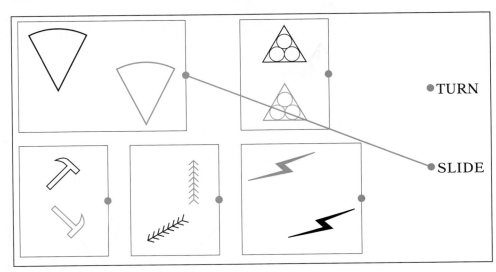

B The pattern on the right has been made using the shape on the left.

1. Which one has been made by sliding the shape?

2. Which one has been made by turning the shape?

A  B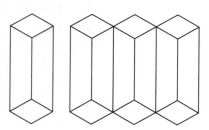

Task 2

Patterns can be made in lots of ways.

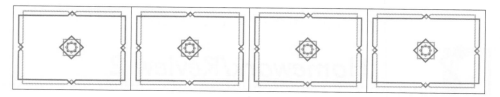

This pattern has been made by sliding a rectangle along.

This pattern has been made by turning a shape.

This shape has been turned by 1, 2 and 3 right angles.

Choose one of the shapes below.
Draw lots of them.
Colour your shapes or put a picture on them.
Make a pattern by sliding or turning your shapes.

Task 3

A Sarah drew two triangles.

She drew a smaller triangle inside each.

She coloured them in 2 ways.

Make lots of triangles like Sarah's.

Colour them in 2 ways.

Make a pattern by sliding or turning them.

B Now cut each triangle in half.

Make a pattern using the halves.

Example

Do this again using a different shape.

Example   You could draw a square inside a square

or you could draw a hexagon inside a hexagon.

CHAPTER REVIEW

Exercise 2
on page 141

A Write down the letters that are beside right angles.

Make a word from these letters.

  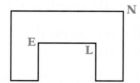

Exercise 3
on page 141

B How many right angles do these have?

1. 2. 3.

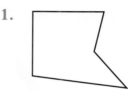 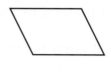 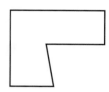

Exercise 4
on page 142

C Is the arrow pointing clockwise or anticlockwise?

1.   2.   3.   4.

Exercise 5
on page 144

D

1 right angle clockwise	3 right angles anticlockwise
2 right angles clockwise	1 right angle anticlockwise

What angle has the black shape been turned by?

Choose from the box.

1.    2.   3.

Exercise 10
on page 148

E Have these shapes been turned or slid?

1.   2.   3.

F

◄◄
Exercise 7
on page 145

		U		R	Q			P	J	
		H	A			C			E	
	L	T	K	S			D			N
		G		I			O		Y	W
↑		V		X	B		Z	M		F

Use a copy of this to find where the chest is buried.
Start at the green square.

> Move 2 squares forward,
> turn 1 right angle clockwise,
> move 5 squares forward,
> turn 1 right angle anticlockwise,
> move 1 square forward,
> turn 3 right angles anticlockwise,
> move 6 squares forward,
> turn 2 right angles clockwise,
> move 3 squares forward.

What letter is in the square where you end?

◄◄
Exercise 11
on page 149

G The pattern on the right has been made using the shape on the left.

1. Which one has been made by turning the shape?

2. Which one has been made by sliding the shape?

A

B

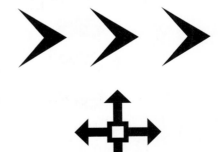

12 Dividing

School camp ....

These are some of the things Kim had to share when she went on school camp.
Draw some other things Kim might have to share on camp.
Draw how they might be shared.

Dividing

There are 12 sweets.
These are shared by 4 girls.
One girl divides the sweets into 4 equal groups.
They get 3 each.

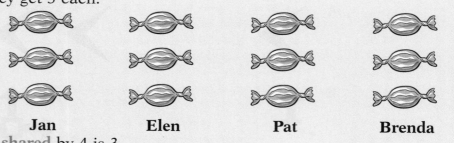

| Jan | Elen | Pat | Brenda |

12 **shared** by 4 is 3.
We could say 12 **divided** by 4 is 3.

How many would each get if there were 20 sweets?

Task

You will need   blocks or counters

A   Take 6 blocks or counters.
If 2 people shared these, how many would each get?
Copy this and fill in the box.   6 shared by 2 is ☐.

If 3 people shared the 6 blocks, how many would each get?
Copy this and fill in the box.   6 shared by 3 is ☐.

B   Take 12 blocks or counters.
Copy these.
   12 divided by 2 is ☐
   12 divided by 3 is ☐
   12 divided by 4 is ☐
   12 divided by 6 is ☐

Divide the 12 blocks into 2 equal piles.
Fill in one of your boxes.

Now divide them into 3 equal piles.
Fill in one of your boxes.

Now divide them into 4 equal piles.
Fill in one of your boxes.

Now divide them into 6 equal piles.
Fill in your last box.

C   Take 20 blocks or counters.
Divide them into equal piles.
Do this as many ways as you can.
Copy these and fill in the boxes.

   20 ÷ ☐ = ☐
   20 ÷ ☐ = ☐
   20 ÷ ☐ = ☐
   20 ÷ ☐ = ☐

Examples   10 shared by 2 = 5.

15 divided by 3 = 5.

Exercise 1

Write down what goes in the gaps.
You can use blocks or counters to help.

1. 8 shared by 2 = _____
2. 8 shared by 4 = _____
3. 12 shared by 3 = _____
4. 12 shared by 4 = _____
5. 12 shared by 6 = _____
6. 16 shared by 4 = _____
7. 20 divided by 5 = _____
8. 30 divided by 3 = _____
9. 24 divided by 4 = _____
10. 10 divided by 5 = _____
11. 18 divided by 3 = _____
12. 24 divided by 3 = _____
13. 21 divided by 3 = _____

12 divided by 4 is 3.
We can write this as $12 \div 4 = 3$.
The ÷ means **divided by**.
We can use the multiplication facts to help check our answers.

×	0	1	2	3	4	5	6	7	8	9	10
2	0	2	4	6	8	10	12	14	16	18	20
3	0	3	6	9	12	15	18	21	24	27	30
4	0	4	8	12	16	20	24	28	32	36	40
5	0	5	10	15	20	25	30	35	40	45	50
10	0	10	20	30	40	50	60	70	80	90	100

Examples We know $4 \times 6 = 24$ We know $3 \times 6 = 18$
So $24 \div 6 = 4$ So $18 \div 6 = 3$

We can write a **family of facts**.
If we know that $3 \times 5 = 15$ then we also know $5 \times 3 = 15$
and $15 \div 3 = 5$ *and* $15 \div 5 = 3$.

Exercise 2

Make a copy of this.

Fill in the boxes to make a family of facts.
The first one is done.

1. $3 \times 2 = 6$ $2 \times 3 = \boxed{6}$
   $6 \div 2 = \boxed{3}$ $\boxed{6} \div 3 = \boxed{2}$

2. $3 \times 4 = \boxed{}$ $4 \times 3 = \boxed{}$
   $12 \div 4 = \boxed{}$ $\boxed{} \div 3 = \boxed{}$

3. $5 \times 7 = \square$ $7 \times 5 = \square$
    $\square \div 7 = \square$ $\square \div 5 = \square$

4. $5 \times 9 = \square$ $9 \times 5 = \square$
    $\square \div 9 = \square$ $\square \div 5 = \square$

5. $3 \times 8 = \square$ $8 \times 3 = \square$
    $\square \div 8 = \square$ $\square \div 3 = \square$

Exercise 3   **A**   Write down the answers to these.

1. $12 \div 2$	2. $6 \div 3$	3. $8 \div 4$
4. $8 \div 2$	5. $12 \div 3$	6. $10 \div 5$
7. $16 \div 4$	8. $14 \div 7$	9. $18 \div 2$
10. $20 \div 5$	11. $20 \div 4$	12. $30 \div 3$
13. $9 \div 3$	14. $15 \div 3$	15. $21 \div 7$
16. $24 \div 4$	17. $18 \div 3$	18. $24 \div 6$
19. $35 \div 5$	20. $50 \div 5$	21. $100 \div 10$
22. $45 \div 9$	23. $35 \div 7$	24. $24 \div 8$
25. $27 \div 3$	26. $30 \div 6$	27. $28 \div 7$
28. $32 \div 8$	29. $36 \div 4$	

B   What number goes in the box?

1. $20 \div \square = 5$	2. $16 \div \square = 4$	3. $24 \div \square = 4$
4. $30 \div \square = 10$	5. $25 \div \square = 5$	6. $27 \div \square = 9$
7. $24 \div \square = 8$	8. $40 \div \square = 8$	9. $35 \div \square = 5$
10. $28 \div \square = 7$	11. $32 \div \square = 8$	

Investigation

If 6 sweets are shared by 6 people, how many do each get?

What does $6 \div 6$ equal?

What about $8 \div 8$, $10 \div 10$, $20 \div 20$, $15 \div 15$?

Copy and finish this sentence.
When we divide a number by itself the answer is always _____.

Exercise 4

Five of these divisions are *not* true.
Write down the letters that are beside these.
Make a word from these letters.

P $21 \div 3 = 7$	**E** $36 \div 9 = 5$	**Q** $50 \div 5 = 10$
T $16 \div 2 = 8$	**I** $30 \div 5 = 6$	**Y** $20 \div 4 = 5$
S $27 \div 3 = 7$	**M** $28 \div 4 = 7$	**H** $9 \div 9 = 0$
L $18 \div 6 = 3$	**B** $35 \div 5 = 7$	**N** $36 \div 4 = 9$
B $24 \div 6 = 4$	**A** $40 \div 4 = 5$	**R** $45 \div 5 = 10$

Exercise 5

Choose numbers from the ring that could fill the boxes.
Do this as many ways as you can.

Two ways are $\boxed{30} \div \boxed{6} = \boxed{5}$ and $\boxed{30} \div \boxed{5} = \boxed{6}$

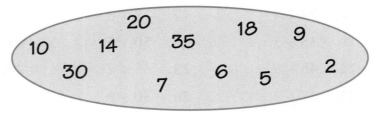

Example   Mary divided her 28 marbles into 4 piles.
How many were in each pile?

Answer   28 divided by 4 is $28 \div 4 = 7$.

Exercise 6

Liz, Zenta and Carl went to a fun park.

A

1.   Liz spent £35 on the Star Wars Ride.
How many rides did she have?

2.   Zenta spent £27 on the Trip to Mars.
How many rides did she have?

B How many pans would this number of people fill?

1. 12   2. 18   3. 21

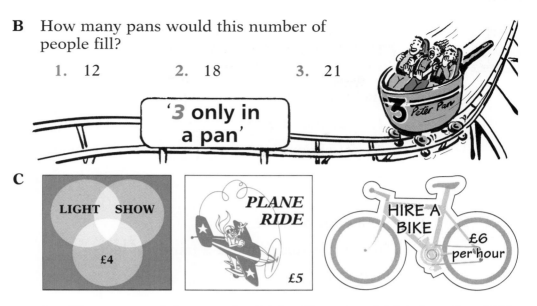

'*3* only in a pan'

C

LIGHT SHOW £4

PLANE RIDE £5

HIRE A BIKE £6 per hour

1. How many tickets to the Light Show could Liz buy for £20?

2. How many plane rides could Zenta have for £45?

3. How many hours could Carl hire a bike for if he paid £24?

Investigation

● 24 people were coming to watch Ben's class play. Ben set out the chairs like this.

How else could he have set out the chairs? Draw pictures.

● 30 people were coming to watch Anne's class play.

Draw pictures to show all the ways she could set out the chairs.

● Draw pictures for some other numbers of people coming to watch a class play.

Homework/Review 1

A What number goes in the gap?

1. 12 shared by 3 = _____
2. 16 shared by 4 = _____
3. 21 shared by 3 = _____
4. 24 divided by 6 = _____
5. 27 divided by 9 = _____
6. 35 divided by 5 = _____

B Use a copy of these.

Fill in the boxes to make a family of facts.

1. 5 × 6 = ☐   6 × 5 = ☐
   ☐ ÷ 6 = 5   ☐ ÷ 5 = ☐

2. 5 × 7 = ☐   7 × 5 = ☐
   ☐ ÷ 7 = ☐   ☐ ÷ 5 = ☐

C **What is a dog after it is a year old?**

Use a copy of the box.

E   8 ÷ 4 = 2
O   12 ÷ 3
S   24 ÷ 3
T   35 ÷ 5
R   36 ÷ 4
A   30 ÷ 6
D   8 ÷ 8
L   50 ÷ 5
Y   24 ÷ 4
W   27 ÷ 9

7	3	4		

	E			
6	2	5	9	8

4	10	1

D 1. May divided her 18 marbles into 2 equal piles.
        How many were in each pile?

    2. Tickets to a show cost £5 each.
       How many could Ravi buy for £30?

Only some numbers can be divided by 2.
Only some numbers can be divided by 5.

Can we divide 7 into 2 equal groups?
Can we divide 8 into 5 equal groups?

Investigation

A

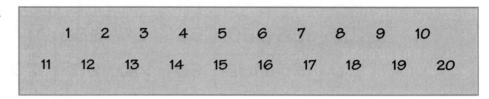

| 1 | 2 | 3 | 4 | 5 | 6 | 7 | 8 | 9 | 10 |
| 11 | 12 | 13 | 14 | 15 | 16 | 17 | 18 | 19 | 20 |

Write down the numbers in the box that can be divided by 2.
Look at these numbers.
Copy and finish this sentence.

If a number can be divided by 2 it is an _____ number.

B

| 5 | 7 | 10 | 14 | 15 | 18 | 20 | 23 | 25 |
| 30 | 33 | 35 | 40 | 42 | 45 | 47 | 50 | |

Write down the numbers from the box than can be divided by 5.
Look at these numbers.
Copy and finish this sentence.

*If a number can be divided by 5, it has a _____ or
a _____ on the end.*

C Write down some numbers that can be divided by 10.
Copy and finish this sentence.

If a number can be divided by 10, it has _____ .

Examples   4, 16, 22, 118, 328 all end in an even number.
They can all be divided by 2.

5, 15, 20, 35, 140, 155 all end in a 5 or a 0.
They can all be divided by 5.

10, 30, 50, 100, 140, 180 all end in a 0.
They can all be divided by 10.

Exercise 7   **A**   Use a copy of the box.
Shade all the numbers that can be divided by 5.

82	53	96	25	112	107	54
217	196	99	50	31	382	117
130	105	100	95	140	275	120
67	102	91	60	101	398	147
88	3	4	125	78	79	104

B   Use another copy of the box.
Shade all the numbers that can be divided by 2.

Exercise 8   **A**   1.   Five friends bought some
bags of sweets to share.
There were 117 sweets.
Will they all get the
same number?
How can you tell?

2.   Two friends shared some bags of sweets.
There were more than 50 sweets.
They both got the same number.
There were none left.
Write down two numbers of sweets they could have shared.

3.   Ten friends bought some bags of sweets to share.
There were 150 sweets.
Will they all get the same number?
How can you tell?

B Five friends shared some bits of chocolate.
They all got the same number of bits.

1. Which of these could be the number of bits?

    25   28   30   45   42   50   48

2. How can you tell which numbers can be divided by 5?

Remainders

Moira had 7 apples.
She shared them with Pete.
They got 3 each and there was 1 left over.

Sometimes when we share or divide, there is some left over.
This is called the remainder.

Example   Eggs are put in boxes of 6.
There are 14 eggs.
How many boxes will be filled?
How many eggs will be left over?

Answer $2 \times 6 = 12$
2 lots of 6 eggs will fill 2 boxes.
$14 - 12 = 2$
There will be 2 left over.

Exercise 9   **A**   Pies are put in boxes of 6.

How many boxes will be filled by these numbers of pies?

How many will be left over?

1. 13   2. 21   3. 16   4. 25

B

TODAY ONLY   BOXES OF PENS   £5

How many boxes can be bought for these amounts?

How much money is left over?

1. £16   2. £23   3. £29   4. £35

C **1.** A bag of 25 apples was shared by 4 people.
They all got the same number.
How many did they each get?
How many were left over?

2. A bag of 33 plums was shared
by 5 people.
They all got the same number.
How many did each get?
How many were left over?

3. A bag of 29 sweets was shared by 3 people.
They all got the same number.
How many did each get?
How many were left over?

Example   Find the remainder of 25 ÷ 4.

Answer   Find a number a bit smaller than 25 that 4 goes into.
24 ÷ 4 = 6.
So there is 1 remainder.

Exercise 10   Find the remainder.

1. 7 ÷ 2	2. 9 ÷ 2	3. 11 ÷ 3	4. 8 ÷ 3
5. 13 ÷ 4	6. 17 ÷ 4	7. 16 ÷ 3	8. 19 ÷ 2
9. 23 ÷ 5	10. 34 ÷ 5	11. 27 ÷ 5	12. 29 ÷ 4
13. 33 ÷ 2	14. 34 ÷ 6	15. 29 ÷ 7	16. 30 ÷ 9
17. 28 ÷ 8	18. 39 ÷ 6	19. 44 ÷ 5	20. 27 ÷ 6

Exercise 11   8 ÷ 5 = 1 with remainder 3
15 ÷ 4 = 3 with remainder 3
23 ÷ 5 = 4 with remainder 3

Make up 2 more divisions which have a remainder of 3.

Puzzle

A class got into twos. One person was left over.
The same class got into threes. One person was left over.
The same class got into fives. No one was left over.
There are less than 40 in the class.
How many are in the class?

Homework/Review 2

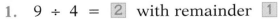

A

| 5 | 8 | 10 | 15 | 40 | 65 | 112 | 125 |

1. Which of these numbers can be divided by 2?
   How can you tell?
2. Which can be divided by 5? How can you tell?
3. Which can be divided by 10? How can you tell?

B Five friends shared some chocolates.
Each friend got the same number.

1. Which of these could have been the
   number of chocolates shared?
   53   55   61   70   85   105

2. How can you tell which numbers
   can be divided by 5?

C 1. Books are put in boxes of 6.
   There are 15 books.
   How many boxes will be filled?
   How many books will be left over?

The Funny Man

STARTS TODAY

Tickets £4

2. How many tickets to The Funny Man
   can be bought with £18?
   How much money is left over?

3. A bag of 42 pears was shared
   by 10 people.
   How many did each get?
   How many were left over?

D Use a copy of this.
Fill in the boxes.
The first one is done.

1. $9 \div 4 =$ 2 with remainder 1
2. $11 \div 3 =$ ☐ with remainder ☐
3. $23 \div 10 =$ ☐ with remainder ☐
4. $28 \div 3 =$ ☐ with remainder ☐
5. $17 \div 4 =$ ☐ with remainder ☐

◀◀ CHAPTER REVIEW ◀◀

◀◀
Exercise 3
on page 157

A Write down the answers to these.

1. 8 ÷ 4   2. 12 ÷ 3   3. 20 ÷ 5
4. 21 ÷ 7   5. 24 ÷ 6   6. 35 ÷ 7

◀◀
Exercise 6
on page 158

B Pam divided her 16 marbles into 4 equal piles.
How many were in each pile?

◀◀
Exercise 7
on page 162

C 1. Use a copy of the box.
Shade all the numbers that can be divided by 5.

20	7	5	9	12	45	19	55	28	21	115	39	120	37
83	135	98	125	101	113	80	11	165	119	36	95	183	105

2. Use another copy of the box.
Shade all the numbers that can be divided by 2.

◀◀
Exercise 8
on page 162

D 1. Two friends bought some bags of sweets to share.
There were 84 sweets.
Will they both get the same number?
How can you tell?

2. Ten friends bought a bag of apples to share.
They all got the same number.
Which of these could be the number of apples?

       21   24   25   30   42   40

How can you tell which numbers can be divided by 10?

◀◀
Exercise 9
on page 163

E Bikes are put in stands of 4.
How many stands will be filled
by these numbers of bikes?
How many will be left over?

1. 17   2. 23   3. 32

◀◀
Exercise 10
on page 164

F Find the remainder.

1. 19 ÷ 3   2. 30 ÷ 4   3. 38 ÷ 5

Quick Test 4

A Write down the answers to these.

1. 10 ÷ 2   2. 16 ÷ 4   3. 20 ÷ 5
4. 24 ÷ 3   5. 30 ÷ 5   6. 50 ÷ 5

B Penny had these tiles.

Use a copy of this tally chart.
Fill it in.

Picture on tile	Tally	Total
flower		
leaf		
blank		

Use a copy of this two-way table.
Fill it in for the tiles.

		picture
		no picture
green	white	

C

1 right angle clockwise	3 right angles anticlockwise
2 right angles clockwise	1 right angle anticlockwise

What angle has the white tile been turned by?
Choose from the box.

1.    2. 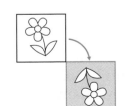   3.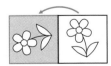

D   How many right angles do these tiles have?

1. 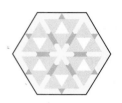   2.    3.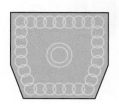

E   The pattern on the right has been made using the tile on the left.

1.   Which has been made by turning the shape?

2.   Which has been made by sliding the shape?

A

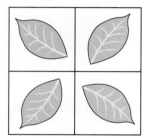

B

F

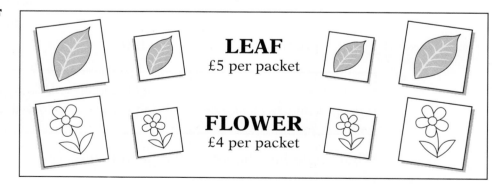

1.   How many packets of the leaf tile can Penny buy for £20?

2.   How many packets of the flower tile can Penny buy for £24?

3.   Ann has £27.
How many packets of flower tiles can she buy?
How much money will she have left?

13 Shapes

At the fair ....

There are lots of different shapes at a fair.
Find as many shapes as you can in the picture.

Shapes

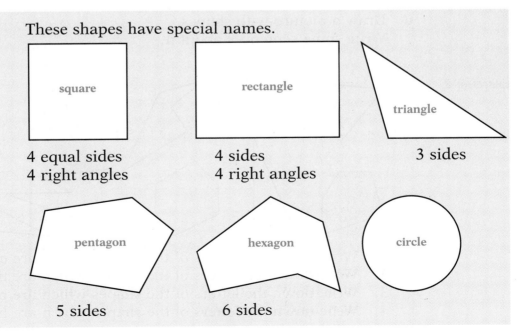

These shapes have special names.

square — 4 equal sides, 4 right angles

rectangle — 4 sides, 4 right angles

triangle — 3 sides

pentagon — 5 sides

hexagon — 6 sides

circle

Exercise 1   **A**

| circle square rectangle triangle pentagon |

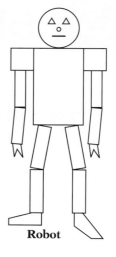

What word goes in the gap?
Choose from the box.
The first one is done.
1. The robot's nose is a __circle__.
2. The robot's body is a _____.
3. The robot's legs are _____.
4. The robot's feet are _____.
5. The robot's head is a _____.
6. The robot's eyes are _____.
7. The robot's shoulders are _____.
8. The robot's hands are _____.

Robot

B

| square   circle   hexagon |
| pentagon   triangle   rectangle |

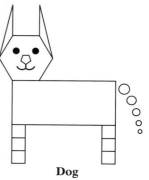

What word goes in the gap?
Choose from the box.
1. The dog's head is a _____.
2. The dog's nose is a _____.
3. The dog's body is a _____.
4. The dog's legs are made from _____.
5. The dog's ears are _____.
6. The dog's tail is made from _____.

Dog

C Draw a picture with shapes.
Write some sentences about it.

Exercise 2

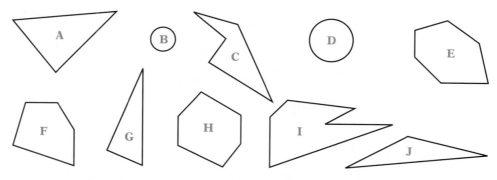

1. Write down the letters of the shapes which are circles.
2. Write down the letters of the shapes which are triangles.
3. Write down the letters of the shapes which are pentagons.
4. Write down the letters of the shapes which are hexagons.

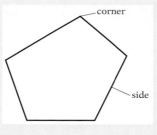

corner

side

This shape has 5 **corners** and 5 **sides**.

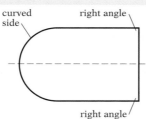

curved side

right angle

right angle

This shape has a **curved side** and two **right angles**.

This shape is also **symmetrical**. It has one line of symmetry.

What other words could you use to tell someone about a shape?

Exercise 3

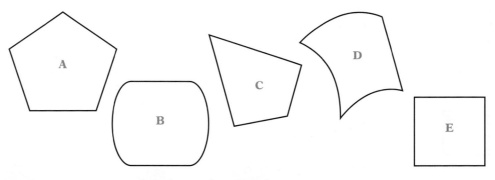

A

B

C

D

E

1. How many sides does shape **A** have?
2. How many sides does shape **B** have?
3. How many curved sides does shape **D** have?
4. How many right angles does shape **E** have?
5. How many lines of symmetry does shape **C** have?
6. How many curved sides does shape **B** have?
7. How many right angles does shape **C** have?

Exercise 4   Write down some sentences about these shapes.

1.

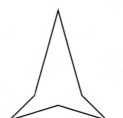

2.

3.

Game for a group: DRAW MY SHAPE

You will need   paper
 a pencil

To play • Choose a leader.
 • The leader draws a shape but keeps it hidden.
 • The leader tells the group about the shape.
 • The rest of the group try to draw it.

Example   Ros was the leader.
 She drew this shape.
 She told the group:
 "It has 3 sides."
 "Two of the sides are straight and one is curved."
 "The two straight sides are the same length."
 • The first person to draw the leader's shape wins.
 • This person is the new leader.

Task 1

Choose **one** of these squares.
Use 20 of them to make patterns.

Examples

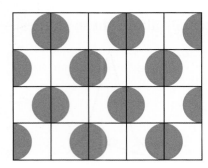 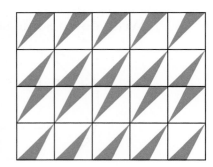

Solids

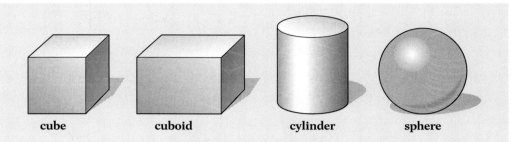

cube   cuboid   cylinder   sphere

What is the difference between a cube and a cuboid?

Look around the room and find some things that are cubes, cuboids, cylinders and spheres.

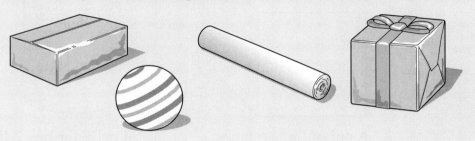

Exercise 5

| sphere | cylinder | cube | cuboid |

What word goes in the gap?
Choose from the box.

1. The tin man's head is a _sphere_ .
2. The tin man's hat is a _____ .
3. The tin man's body is a _____ .
4. The tin man's legs are _____ .
5. The tin man's feet are _____ .
6. The tin man's hands are _____ .
7. The tin man's arms are _____ .
8. The tin man's neck is a _____ .

Tin man

Exercise 6   Name each of these solids.

1.   2.   3.   4.

5.   6.   7.   8.

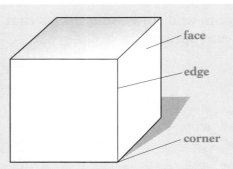
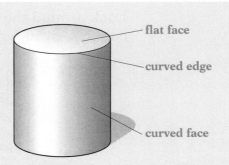

A cuboid has 6 faces,
12 edges and 8 corners.

A cylinder has 2 flat faces,
1 curved face and 2 curved edges.

How many faces does a sphere have?
How many edges does a sphere have?

Exercise 7   What goes in the gap?

A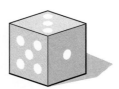
1. This dice has _____ faces.
2. This dice has _____ edges.
3. This dice has _____ corners.

B
1. This tin has _____ faces.
2. This tin has _____ edges.
3. This tin has _____ corners.

C
1. This cheese has _____ faces.
2. This cheese has _____ edges.
3. This cheese has _____ corners.

Task 2

You will need multilink cubes or lego blocks
a friend to work with

A Make a solid using 5 cubes.
Don't let your friend see it.
Tell your friend how to make it.
Do this 3 times each.
Who got most right?

B Use 4 cubes to make solids.
Make as many different solids as you can.
Don't let your friend see.
Who made the most?

Now try this again using 5 cubes.

Game for a group: WHAT IS MY NAME?

You will need pencil
paper

To play • Choose someone to start.

• This person chooses a solid and tells the group about it.

Example

If this is the solid, the person might say:

  "It has a circle at each end."

  "It has a curved surface."

  "It has no corners."

• The player who guesses it first gets 1 point.

• Each person has a turn at choosing a solid.

Homework/Review 1

A

| circle | pentagon | triangle | hexagon |

What word goes in the gap?
Choose from the box.
1. The eyes are _circles_ .
2. The ears are _____.
3. The head is a _____.
4. The trunk is a _____.
5. The tusks are _____.

B

A   B   C   D   E

1. How many sides does shape **B** have?
2. How many sides does shape **D** have?
3. How many lines of symmetry does shape **A** have?
4. How many curved sides does shape **C** have?
5. How many right angles does shape **E** have?

C Name each of these solids.
Choose from the words in the box.

1.   2.   3.

| cube |
| cylinder |
| cuboid |
| sphere |

4. Chocolates   5. Fruit Salad   6.

D P   Q   R

What number goes in the gap?
1. Shape **P** has _____ faces.
2. Shape **Q** has _____ curved face.
3. Shape **R** has _____ edges.
4. Shape **R** has _____ corners.

Sorting shapes

We can sort shapes into groups.

Examples

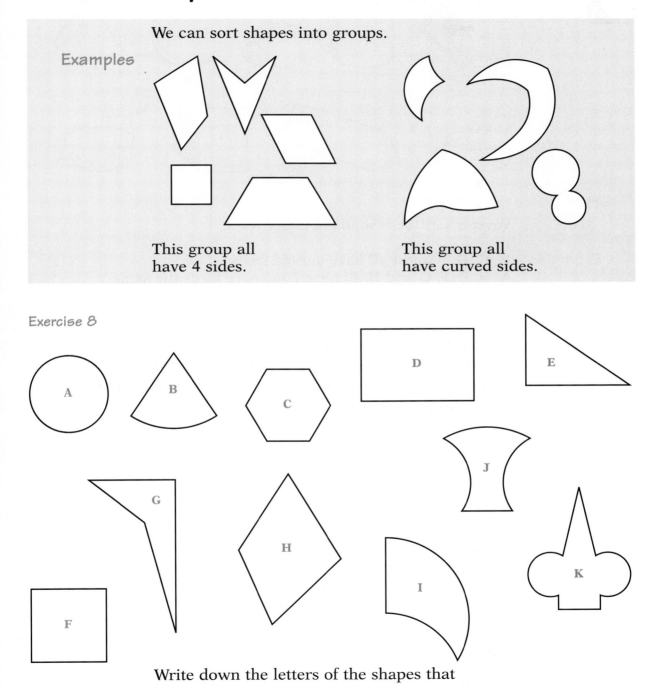

This group all
have 4 sides.

This group all
have curved sides.

Exercise 8

Write down the letters of the shapes that

1. have 4 sides
2. have all straight sides
3. have some curved sides
4. are symmetrical
5. have no corners
6. have right angles

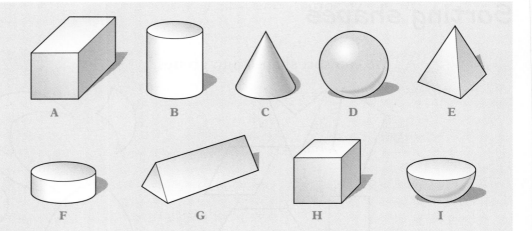

We can sort these solids in many ways.

Examples   B, C, D, F and I all have curved faces.
A, B, E, F, G and H all have 2 or more faces the same.

Exercise 9   Write down the letters of the solids above that
1.   can roll easily   2.   have corners
3.   have more than 2 faces   4.   has no edges
5.   do not have curved faces 6.   have no faces the same
7.   have a triangle for 1 or more faces

Exercise 10   **A**   Zenta sorted some shapes into three groups.

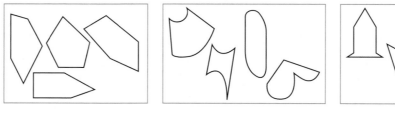

Group A   **Group B**   **Group C**

Which group do these shapes go in? How can you tell?

1.   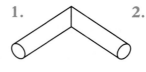   2.   3.      4.

B Gwyn sorted some shapes into 3 groups.

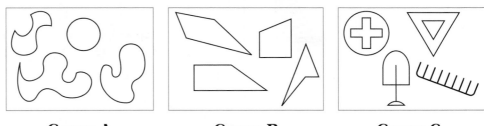

| **Group A** | **Group B** | **Group C** |

1. What letter goes in the gap?

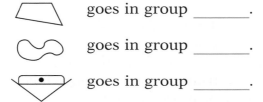

goes in group _____.

goes in group _____.

goes in group _____.

2. This shape could go in group B or group C.

Why does it fit in group B?

Why does it fit in group C?

Homework/Review 2

A

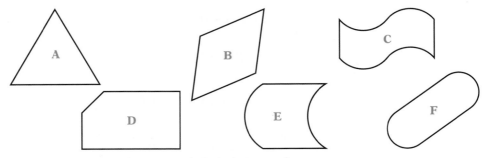

Write down the letters of the shapes that

1. have curved sides
2. have 1 or more right angles
3. have 4 sides
4. are not symmetrical
5. do not have all straight sides

B

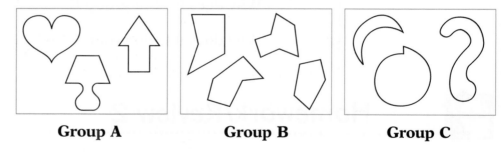

Write down the letters of the solids
1. that have corners
2. that have 2 or more faces the same
3. that have a triangle for 1 or more faces
4. that have 1 or more curved faces.

C Sam sorted some shapes into 3 groups.

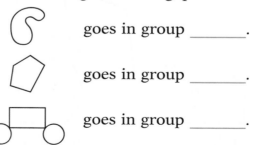

Group A   **Group B**   **Group C**

1. What letter goes in the gap?

goes in group _____ .

goes in group _____ .

goes in group _____ .

2. This shape could go in group A or B.

Why does it fit in group A?

Why does it fit in group B?

◄◄ CHAPTER REVIEW ◄◄

◄ ◄
Exercise 2
on page 170

A Use a copy of this table.
Fill it in.
A has been done.

Shape	Letters
circles	A
pentagons	
hexagons	
squares	
triangles	

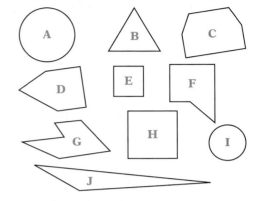

◄◄
Exercise 3
on page 171

B

1. How many sides does shape **C** have?
2. How many curved sides does shape **B** have?
3. How many lines of symmetry does shape **A** have?
4. How many right angles does shape **D** have?

◄◄
Exercise 6
on page 174

C Name each of these solids.

1.
2.
3.
4.

◄◄
Exercise 8
on page 177

D

1. Write down the letters of the shapes which have some curved sides.
2. Write down the letters of the shapes that have 4 sides.
3. Write down the letters of the shapes that are symmetrical.
4. Write down the letters of the shapes that have 1 or more right angles.

◄◄
Exercise 9
on page 178

E Find the words that go with each solid.
The answer to **1.** is **A, B, C, D, F.**

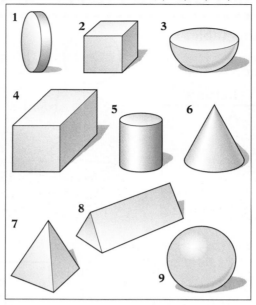

A can roll easily

B does not have corners

C has 1 or more curved faces

D has edges

E does not have edges

F has 2 or more faces the same

◄◄
Exercise 10
on page 178

F Mindu sorted some shapes into 3 groups.

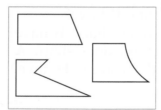

Group A   **Group B**   **Group C**

What letter goes in the gap?

1. [shape] goes in group _____.

2. [shape] goes in group _____.

3. [shape] goes in group _____.

◄◄
Exercise 10
on page 178

G   This shape could go in group A or group C.
Why does it fit in group A?
Why does it fit in group C?

Using the Calculator

Saving time..

People often use a calculator to save time.

When might these people use a calculator?

- farmers
- bankers
- builders

- teachers
- nurses
- painters

- gardeners
- police
- engineers

Using a calculator

+ is the addition key.

− is the subtraction key.

× is the multiplication key.

÷ is the division key.

= is pressed to get the answer.

Examples   37 + 64 is keyed as   **3**   **7**   **+**   **6**   **4**   **=**

322 ÷ 14 is keyed as   **3**   **2**   **2**   **÷**   **1**   **4**   **=**

What are the answers to these?

Exercise 1   Use a calculator to find the answers to these.

1. 23 + 61	2. 38 + 84	3. 87 + 92
4. 321 + 642	5. 85 − 62	6. 79 − 32
7. 183 − 57	8. 532 − 429	9. 9 × 12
10. 23 × 8	11. 15 × 16	12. 27 × 32
13. 39 ÷ 13	14. 147 ÷ 7	15. 338 ÷ 26
16. 621 ÷ 27	17. 187 + 65	18. 527 − 322
19. 984 ÷ 41	20. 56 × 15	21. 38 × 22
22. 350 ÷ 14	23. 961 − 724	24. 96 + 35

Exercise 2   Use a copy of these.

Fill them in.

1.

+	27	84	352
142			
479			
381			

2.

×	14	23	19
36			
42			
29			

3.

+		142	385
346	789		
		321	
			891

Exercise 3   Use a copy of this crossnumber.

Fill it in.

Across	**Down**
1. 968 ÷ 8	1. 784 ÷ 4
4. 926 − 489	2. 134 − 108
7. 999 − 33	3. 489 ÷ 3
8. 505 − 89	4. 828 − 386
9. 783 − 441	5. 527 ÷ 17
13. 945 ÷ 9	6. 987 − 224
15. 921 − 189	10. 882 ÷ 21
17. 899 ÷ 29	11. 824 ÷ 8
18. 819 ÷ 39	12. 924 ÷ 7
	14. 757 − 238
	16. 852 ÷ 4

Remember . . .

In **magic squares** we get the same answer no matter which way we add.

Exercise 4

Use a copy of these magic squares.

Fill them in.

1.

24	4	17
13		

2.

131		
	79	
56		27

3.

		64
		47
26		24

Investigation

Use each of the buttons 2 5 3 just once

with any of these buttons + − × ÷ =

Examples   2 × 3 × 5 =   5 3 × 2 =

5 × 3 + 2 =

What is the biggest number you can make?

Now try 8 6 3 instead of 2 5 and 3

Try 9 4 1

and 7 6 2

and 9 7 3

Is the biggest number always made the same way?

Game for any number of players: SMALLEST

You will need   a pen or pencil
a calculator
some copies of this board

START

		999			
	32	54	71		
	64	89	61	23	94
104	82	31	89	32	74	106
64	32	91	85	94	79	53	52	87
41	99	79	16	32	106	41	33	92	86	14

To play   • Wait for your teacher to say "Go".

• Start at the top at 999.

• Move down the board.

You may move   ↓   or   →   or   ←

but **not**   ↑   or   ↗   or   ↙   or   ↘   or   ↙

• Subtract each number you move to.

• Write down the answer at the end.

Example   999–54–32–89–64–82–104–32–91–16–79 = 356

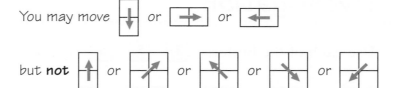

• Find as many answers as you can until your teacher says "Stop".

• The winner is the person who has found the smallest answer.

Example   Steve bought a walkman for £34
and a clock for £16.

How much did this
cost altogether?

Answer   We must add 34 and 16.

34 + 16 = 50

It cost £50.

Exercise 5

radio
£25

discman
£89

stereo
£179

CDs
£11

1.   Mike bought a radio and a stereo.
How much did these cost?

2.   Lisa bought a discman and a CD.
How much did these cost?

3.   Meg bought a stereo and a CD.
How much did these cost?

Example   Jim bought a watch for £49.
His mother paid £23 of this.
How much did Jim pay?

Answer   We must subtract 23 from 49.

49 – 23 = 26

He paid £26.

Exercise 6   1.   Tim bought a stereo for £179.
His mother paid £96 of this.
How much did Tim pay?

2.   Nerys bought a TV for £149.
Her mother paid £87 of this.
How much did Nerys pay?

3.   Pat bought a tent for £359.
Her brother paid £169 of this.
How much did Pat pay?

Example   Sam put 14 cakes on each plate.
How many are there on 11 plates?

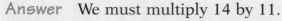

Answer   We must multiply 14 by 11.

$14 \times 11 = 154$ | 1 | 4 | × | 1 | 1 | = |

Exercise 7   **A**   17 books will fit on a shelf.
How many books will fit on
   1. 8 shelves   2. 27 shelves   3. 16 shelves?

B   A row has 15 seats.
How many seats are there in
   1. 20 rows   2. 18 rows   3. 29 rows?

Example   A bus holds 27 people.
How many buses are needed for 135 people?

Answer   We must divide 135 by 27.

$135 \div 27 = 5$ | 1 | 3 | 5 | ÷ | 2 | 7 | = |

Exercise 8   1. A bus holds 32 people.
How many buses are needed for 224 people?
2. A bus holds 38 people.
How many buses are needed for 342 people?
3. A bus holds 54 people.
How many buses are needed for 594 people?

Sometimes we must work out if we have to add,
subtract, multiply or divide.

Exercise 9   1. Tom planted 11 rows of carrots.
There were 27 in each row.
How many carrots were there altogether?
2. Sue had 29 sweets in one bag and 37 in the other.
How many sweets did she have altogether?
3. Nesta has 300 sweets.
She wants to put them into bags with 25 in each bag.
How many bags will she need?
4. Dan had £875. He spent £328.
How much did he have left?

Homework/Review 1

A Use a copy of these.
Fill them in.

1.

+	154	114	286
89			
159			
93			

2.

×	27	18	31
17			
32			
22			

B **What has four legs
and can see just as
well from both ends?**

Use a copy of this box.

I	27 + 32 = 59
S	324 − 186
U	52 × 17
A	98 × 7
E	448 ÷ 14
R	851 ÷ 37
W	319 + 569
T	37 × 27
O	988 ÷ 19
Y	596 − 389
H	897 − 389

$\overline{686}\quad\overline{508}\quad\overline{52}\quad\overline{23}\quad\overline{138}\quad\overline{32}$

$\overset{I}{\underset{888}{\rule{0pt}{0pt}}}\quad\overline{59}\quad\overline{999}\quad\overline{508}\qquad\overset{I}{\underset{59}{\rule{0pt}{0pt}}}\quad\overline{999}\quad\overline{138}$

$\overline{32}\quad\overline{207}\quad\overline{32}\quad\overline{138}\qquad\overline{138}\quad\overline{508}\quad\overline{884}\quad\overline{999}$

C 1. Anna's street has 87 houses on one side and 96 on the other.
How many houses are there altogether?

2. Karen put 21 cakes on each plate.
How many are there on 32 plates?

3. There were 187 cars for sale. 59 were sold.
How many were left?

4. A bus holds 46 people.
How many buses are needed for 552 people?

Checking answers

When we use a calculator it is easy to press a wrong button.
We must always **check the answer**.
We can do this by **undoing** what we did.

Example   6 + 8 = 14   add 8
14 − 8 = 6   subtract 8 from the answer
we get back to 6

Subtracting **undoes** adding.
What undoes subtracting?

Example   37 + 25
Ben did this on his calculator and got 62. Is he right?

Answer   Ben added 25.
To check we must subtract 25 from his answer.

| 6 | 2 | − | 2 | 5 | = | **37.** |

So Ben has the right answer.

Example   185 − 96
Claire did this on her calculator and got 116. Is she right?

Answer   Claire subtracted 96.
We must add 96 to the answer.

| 1 | 1 | 6 | + | 9 | 6 | = | **212.** |

We do not get back to 185. So Claire's answer is wrong.

Exercise 10   Amy did some sums.
Then she checked them.

Use a copy of this.
Fill in the calculator buttons.
Did Amy get her sums right?

1.   86 + 37 = 123
To check Amy pressed   1 2 3 ☐ 3 7 =

2.   389 + 427 = 861
To check Amy pressed   8 6 1 ☐ ☐ ☐ ☐ =

3. $583 - 279 = 304$
   To check Amy pressed [3] [0] [4] [ ] [2] [7] [9] [=]

4. $694 - 391 = 258$
   To check Amy pressed [2] [5] [8] [ ] [ ] [ ] [ ] [=]

Example $5 \times 3 = 15$ multiply by 3
         $15 \div 3 = 5$ divide the answer by 3
                                 we get back to 5

Dividing **undoes** multiplying.
What undoes dividing?

Example 12×9
         Carol did this on her calculator and got 108.
         Is she right?

Answer   Carol multiplied by 9.
         To check, we must divide her answer by 9.

         [1] [0] [8] [÷] [9] [=] | 12. |

         So Carol has the right answer.

Example $541 \div 11$
         Ravi did this on his calculator and got 41. Is he right?

Answer   Ravi divided by 11.
         To check his answer, we must multiply it by 11.

         [4] [1] [×] [1] [1] [=] | 451. |

         We did not get back to 541.
         So Ravi's answer is wrong.

Exercise 11   Ravi did some sums.
               Then he checked them.

               Use a copy of this.
               Fill in the calculator buttons.
               Did Ravi get his sums right?

               1. $14 \times 13 = 128$
                  To check Ravi pressed [1] [2] [8] [ ] [1] [3] [=]

2. $18 \times 23 = 414$
   To check Ravi pressed 4 1 4 ▢ ▢ ▢ =

3. $288 \div 24 = 12$
   To check Ravi pressed 1 2 ▢ 2 4 =

4. $500 \div 25 = 25$
   To check Ravi pressed 2 5 ▢ ▢ ▢ =

5. $27 \times 19 = 486$
   To check Ravi pressed 4 8 6 ▢ ▢ ▢ =

Exercise 12

Use a copy of this.
Fill in the boxes.

1. 2 7 + 3 3 = | 60. |
   6 0 ▢ ▢ ▢ = | 27. |

2. 1 7 × 5 = | 85. |
   8 5 ▢ ▢ = | 17. |

3. 9 5 − 2 3 = | 72. |
   7 2 ▢ ▢ ▢ = | 95. |

4. 6 0 ÷ 4 = | 15. |
   1 5 ▢ ▢ = | 60. |

5. 1 3 × 4 = | 52. |
   5 2 ▢ ▢ = | 13. |

Homework/Review 2

A Ben did some sums.
Then he checked them.

Use a copy of this.
Fill in the calculator buttons.
Did Ben get his sums right?

1. 89 + 12 = 101
To check Ben pressed **1** **0** **1** ☐ **1** **2** **=**

2. 256 – 138 = 73
To check Ben pressed **7** **3** ☐ ☐ ☐ ☐ **=**

3. 18 × 23 = 576
To check Ben pressed **5** **7** **6** ☐ **2** **3** **=**

4. 123 ÷ 41 = 3
To check Ben pressed **3** ☐ ☐ ☐ **=**

B Use a copy of this.
Fill in the boxes.

1. **8** **3** **–** **2** **9** **=** | *54.* |
5 **4** ☐ ☐ ☐ **=** | *83.* |

2. **1** **6** **×** **5** **=** | *80.* |
8 **0** ☐ ☐ **=** | *16.* |

3. **1** **2** **4** **+** **8** **6** **=** | *210.* |
2 **1** **0** ☐ ☐ ☐ **=** | *124.* |

4. **7** **5** **÷** **5** **=** | *15.* |
1 **5** ☐ ☐ **=** | *75.* |

◀◀ CHAPTER REVIEW ◀◀

◀◀
Exercise 1
on page 184

A Use a calculator to find the answers to these.

1. 57 + 29
2. 82 − 39
3. 13 × 9
4. 90 ÷ 6
5. 883 − 569
6. 23 × 21
7. 304 ÷ 19

◀◀
Exercise 2
on page 184

B Use a copy of these.
Fill them in.

+	36	52	427
361			
297			
462			

×	16	24	18
37			
41			
26			

+	325		187
	864		
296	573		
			694

◀◀
Exercise 9
on page 188

C
1. A taxi holds 5 people.
   How many taxis are needed for 70 people?
2. Rob had 18 birds in one cage and 27 in the other.
   How many birds did he have altogether?
3. Dele had £382. He spent £296.
   How much did he have left?
4. Lorna bought 14 bags of sweets.
   Each bag had 24 sweets.
   How many sweets did she buy?

◀◀
Exercises 10
and 11
on pages 190
and 191

D Laura did some sums.
Then she checked them.

Use a copy of this.
Fill in the boxes.
Are Laura's answers right?
1. 57 + 92 = 149
   To check Laura pressed `1` `4` `9` `☐` `☐` `☐` `=`
2. 29 × 19 = 515
   To check Laura pressed `5` `1` `5` `☐` `☐` `☐` `=`

◀◀
Exercise 12
on page 192

E Use a copy of this.
Fill in the boxes.

`9` `2` `−` `3` `6` `=` | 56.
`5` `6` `☐` `☐` `☐` `=` | 92.

15

Rounding

About...

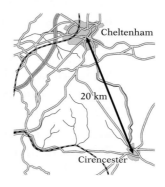

Tom said, "My grandmother is **about** 80".

Julie said, "It is **about** 20 km to the next town".

Dele said, "I have got **about** £40 in the bank".

Write a sentence with **about** in it for these.

- people at a football game
- pupils in a school
- cars in a car park

- distance to the next town
- age of a school

To the nearest ten

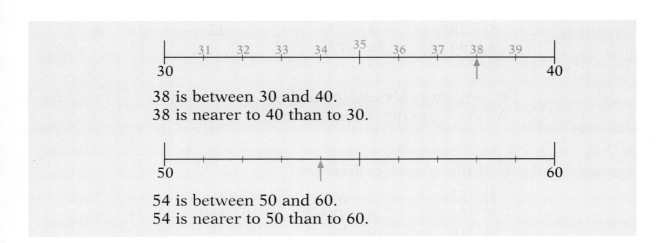

38 is between 30 and 40.
38 is nearer to 40 than to 30.

54 is between 50 and 60.
54 is nearer to 50 than to 60.

Exercise 1   Write down what goes in the gaps.
The first one is done.
1.   39 is between __30__ and __40__.
2.   42 is between _____ and _____.
3.   56 is between _____ and _____.
4.   18 is between _____ and _____.
5.   91 is between _____ and _____.
6.   77 is between _____ and _____.

Exercise 2   Write down what goes in the gaps.
The first one is done.
1.   39 is nearer to __40__ than to __30__.
2.   42 is nearer to _____ than to _____.
3.   56 is nearer to _____ than to _____.
4.   18 is nearer to _____ than to _____.
5.   91 is nearer to _____ than to _____.
6.   77 is nearer to _____ than to _____.

We don't always give an exact answer.
Sometimes we give a number **to the nearest ten**.

Example   Give 67 to the nearest ten.

Answer   67 is nearer to 70 than to 60.
So 67, to the nearest ten, is 70.

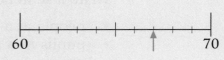

Exercise 3   Give these to the nearest ten.

1. 57	2. 81	3. 48	4. 32
5. 28	6. 17	7. 12	8. 8
9. 69	10. 72		

45 is halfway between 40 and 50.
We say 45, to the nearest ten, is 50.

Exercise 4   Give these to the nearest ten.

1. 55	2. 65	3. 15	4. 75
5. 21	6. 38	7. 85	8. 93
9. 19	10. 77	11. 35	

Example   Give 127 to the nearest ten.

Answer   127 is between 120 and 130.
            127 is nearer to 130 than to 120.
            So 127, to the nearest ten, is 130.

            120   130

Exercise 5   Give these to the nearest ten.

1.	121	2.	129	3.	132	4.	138
5.	153	6.	178	7.	194	8.	186
9.	125	10.	175	11.	236	12.	384
13.	451	14.	569	15.	655		

Example

178 PEOPLE AT GAME

Give this to the nearest 10.

Answer   178 is closer to 180 than 170.
            178, to the nearest 10, is 180.

Exercise 6   Write the numbers in these to the nearest ten.

1.  87 GIRLS AT CAMP   2. 91 CARS IN SMASH   3.  267 WINNERS

4. MONEY HELPS 475   5. £507 SPENT ON FLOWERS   6.  CAR SELLS FOR £325

To the nearest hundred

Sometimes we give a number **to the nearest hundred**.

200   210 220 230 240 250 260 270 280 290   300

220 is between 200 and 300.
220 is nearer to 200 than to 300.
220, to the nearest hundred, is 200.

Exercise 7

| 100 | 200 | 300 | 400 | 500 | 600 | 700 | 800 | 900 |

Write down what goes in the gaps.
Choose from the box.
The first one is done.

1. 314 is nearer to __300__ than to __400__ .
2. 187 is nearer to _____ than to _____ .
3. 562 is nearer to _____ than to _____ .
4. 421 is nearer to _____ than to _____ .
5. 885 is nearer to _____ than to _____ .
6. 710 is nearer to _____ than to _____ .
7. 480 is nearer to _____ than to _____ .
8. 230 is nearer to _____ than to _____ .

450 is halfway between 400 and 500.
We say 450, to the nearest hundred, is 500.

Examples   150, to the nearest hundred, is 200.
750, to the nearest hundred, is 800.
650, to the nearest hundred, is 700.

Exercise 8   Give these to the nearest hundred.

1. 120   2. 280   3. 364   4. 571
5. 416   6. 733   7. 859   8. 765
9. 145   10. 350   11. 650   12. 104
13. 399 14. 89   15. 50

Example   There were 579 people at a tennis game.
Give this to the nearest hundred.

Answer   579, to the nearest hundred, is 600.

Exercise 9   Write the numbers in these to the nearest hundred.

1.
SMALL GIRL WINS £468

2. 114 AT OPENING

3.
87 LOSE MONEY

4. 308 ON PLANE

5. 276 AT SALE

6.
£329 GOES TO SCHOOL

Exercise 10 **A** A number, given to the nearest ten, is 50.
Which of these numbers could it be?
There is more than one answer.

47   41   53   51   56   55   45

B A number, given to the nearest hundred, is 300.
Which of these numbers could it be?
There is more than one answer.

308   287   249   352   389   327   350   250

Task

You will need   a pencil and paper
poster paper
coloured pens or pencils

Find out the answers to these.

How many pupils are in
your class?

How many pupils are in
your school?

How many pupils in your
school play football?

How many pupils in your
school play netball?

How many pupils in your
school play cricket?

How many pupils in your school play tennis?

Make a poster to show what you found. Give all the numbers on
your poster to the nearest ten or nearest hundred.

You could make up some different questions about your school.

Homework/Review 1

A Use a copy of this.
Fill in the gaps.
The first one is done.

1. 58 is nearer to ___60___ than to ___50___ .
2. 41 is nearer to _____ than to _____ .
3. 17 is nearer to _____ than to _____ .
4. 22 is nearer to _____ than to _____ .
5. 89 is nearer to _____ than to _____ .

B Give these to the nearest ten.

   1. 67   2. 21   3. 14   4. 89
   5. 55   6. 25   7. 19   8. 85

C Write the numbers in these to the nearest ten.
1. There were 64 people at a football game.
2. Val has 187 stamps.
3. David's bike cost £418.

D **What bank do computers keep their money in?**

Use a copy of this box.
Give these to the nearest hundred.

N 743
Y 381
K 789
E 455
O 320
R 150
A 111
B 550
M 852

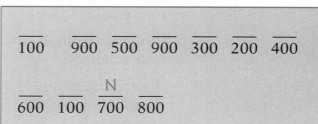

__ __ __ __ __ __ __
100 900 500 900 300 200 400

__ __ N __
600 100 700 800

E Write the numbers in these to the nearest hundred.

1. There were 161 people at a tennis game.
2. There were 311 people on a plane.

F A number given to the nearest ten is 140.
Which of these numbers could it be?
There is more than one answer.

      135   125   143   148   145   137

Game for 2 players: NEAREST

You will need 2 dice
red counters
green counters
this board

10	50	40	70	50	70	10	70	50	60	60	20
60	40	20	30	10	30	10	50	30	20	30	10
40	70	30	40	50	60	20	10	20	10	70	30
50	60	70	50	40	30	40	50	40	20	30	20
40	20	10	60	70	60	20	40	70	30	10	60

To play   •   Roll the 2 dice.
• Write down the two numbers you can make.

Example Sue rolled these.

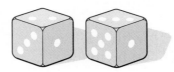

She wrote down 23 and 32.

• Choose **one** of the numbers.
Give it to the nearest 10.
Put a counter on this.

Example Sue chose 23.
23, to the nearest 10, is 20.
Sue put a counter on 20.
• The winner is the first person to get 3 counters in a line.

A line is

Left overs

Jake's class went to the cinema by car.
There were 22 in the class.
Each car took 4 people.
How many cars were needed?

When we divide 22 by 4 we get 5 with 2 left over.
Does this mean they needed 5 cars?
What about the 2 left over?

Pizzas cost £4.
Each person in Jake's class put in £1.
They then had £22.
How many could they buy?

When we divide 22 by 4 we
get 5 with 2 left over.
Does this mean they could buy 5 pizzas?
What about the 2 left over?

Example Balloons are tied in lots of 3.
How many lots can be made
from 13 balloons?

Answer 13 ÷ 3 = 4 with 1 left over.
So 4 lots can be made.

Example Cans of drink come in packs of 6.
How many packs are needed for 20 people?

Answer 20 ÷ 6 = 3 with 2 left over.
If we just get 3 packs then 2 people miss out.
So we have to add one more to get 4 packs.

Exercise 11   **A** Buttons come in cards of 5.
How many cards must be bought to get

1. 7 buttons

2. 11 buttons

3. 13 buttons?

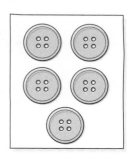

B Buns come in packs of 6.
How many buns are needed for these?

  1. 13 people

  2. 19 people

  3. 32 people

C 4 people can ride in a taxi.
How many taxis are needed for this many?

  1. 9   **2.** 14   **3.** 23

D How many tickets
can be bought for

  1. £7

  2. £13

  3. £20?

E How many cans of paint must be bought to get

  1. 15 litres   **2.** 23 litres   **3.** 19 litres?

F 5 people are needed to make a maths team.
How many teams can be made from

  1. 18 people   **2.** 24 people   **3.** 27 people?

G 3 people can sit on a seat.
How many seats are needed for

  1. 13 people

  2. 19 people

  3. 26 people?

Homework/Review 2

**What has two wings
but doesn't fly?**

$$\frac{A}{4} \quad \frac{}{6} \quad \frac{}{2} \quad \frac{}{1} \quad \frac{}{9} \quad \frac{}{5} \quad \frac{}{3} \quad \frac{}{8} \quad \frac{}{5} \quad \frac{A}{4} \quad \frac{}{7}$$

Use a copy of this box.

A Balloons are tied in lots of 5.
How many lots can be made from 23 balloons?

O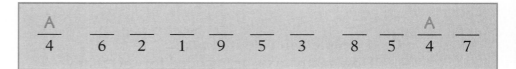

How many pizzas can be bought for £11?

E Cans of drink come in packs of 6.
How many packs are needed for 25 people?

Y 4 people can ride in a taxi.
How many taxis are needed for 11 people?

C

How many tickets can be bought for £15?

M Mary needs 13 litres of paint for a fence.
How many 2 litre tins will she need to buy?

H Dean needs 23 litres of paint for his house.
How many 4 litre tins will he need to buy?

T 3 people are needed to make a maths team.
How many teams can be made from 26 people?

K 2 people are needed to make a spelling team.
How many teams can be made from 19 people?

◄◄ CHAPTER REVIEW ◄◄

Exercise 2
on page 196

A Use a copy of this
Fill in the gaps.
The first one is done.
1. 56 is nearer to ___60___ than to ___50___ .
2. 81 is nearer to _____ than to _____ .
3. 17 is nearer to _____ than to _____ .

Exercises 3
and 4
on page 196

B Give these to the nearest ten.
1. 78   2. 31   3. 54   4. 86
5. 65   6. 75   7. 22   8. 15

Exercise 5
on page 197

C Give these to the nearest ten.
1. 128   2. 271   3. 486   4. 314

Exercise 6
on page 197

D Write the numbers in these to the nearest ten.
1. There were 41 people at a hockey game.
2. Amy has 125 stamps.
3. Ali's bike cost £258.

Exercise 7
on page 198

E Use a copy of this.
Fill in the gaps.
The first one is done.
1. 329 is nearer to ___300___ than to ___400___ .
2. 578 is nearer to _____ than to _____ .
3. 771 is nearer to _____ than to _____ .

Exercise 8
on page 198

F Give these to the nearest hundred.
1. 170   2. 230   3. 341   4. 576
5. 850   6. 304   7. 550

Exercise 9
on page 198

G Write the numbers in these to the nearest hundred.
1. There were 638 people on a ship.
2. There were 364 people on a plane.

Exercise 10
on page 199

H 1. A number, given to the nearest ten, is 40.
Which of these numbers could it be?
There is more than one answer.

37   42   32   46   45   35

2. A number, given to the nearest hundred, is 500.
Which of these numbers could it be?
There is more than one answer.

497   503   445   535   563   550   450

Exercise 11
on page 202

I 1. Balloons are tied in lots of 5.
How many lots can be made from 18 balloons?

2. Cans of drink come in packs of 4.
How many packs are needed for 13 people?

3. 5 people can ride in a taxi.
How many taxis are needed for 14 people?

4. A disco costs £6.
How many tickets can be bought for £20?

5. 4 people can go in each car in a ride at a fair.
How many cars are needed for 15 people?

Quick Test 5

A Sam's school had these
shapes painted on a wall.
Use a copy of the table.
Fill in the letters.
A has been done for you.

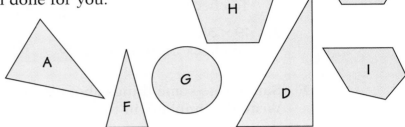

Shape	Letters
circles	
triangles	A
pentagons	
hexagons	

B | cube   cuboid   cylinder   sphere |

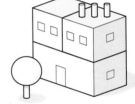

Sam made a model of a school building.
What word goes in the gap?
Choose from the box.

1. He made the bottom storey from a _cuboid_.

2. He made the top storey from two _____.

3. He made the chimneys from _____.

4. He made the tree top from a _____.

C In maths, Sam sorted shapes into 3 groups.

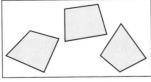

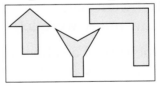

Group A   **Group B**   **Group C**

What letter goes in the gap?

1.   goes in group ____.   2. goes in group ____.

3.   goes in groups A and B.
Explain why it fits in group A.
Explain why it fits in group B.

D   Use a calculator to find the answers to these.
  1. 87 + 129
  2. 386 – 297
  3. 34 × 12
  4. 368 ÷ 16
  5. 15 × 15
  6. 389 + 264

E   Sam did some sums. Then he checked them.
Use a copy of this. Fill in the boxes.
Are Sam's answers right?

  1. 684 – 389 = 286
     To check Sam pressed   [2] [8] [6] [ ] [ ] [ ] [ ] [=]

  2. 19 × 32 = 608
     To check Sam pressed   [6] [0] [8] [ ] [ ] [ ] [=]

F   Sam wrote some things about his school.
Write the numbers in these to the nearest ten.

> 1. There are 479 pupils at my school.
> 2. There are 17 teachers at my school.

G   Write the numbers in these to the nearest hundred.

> 1. There are 782 books in the school library.
> 2. There are 250 pupils in Years 7 and 8.

H   1. One side of the hall had 279 pupils.
The other had 168.
How many pupils were there altogether?

  2. There were 385 pupils in the hall.
169 went out.
How many were left?

  3. One row of a school hall holds 15 pupils.
How many pupils can 28 rows hold?

  4. One row of a school hall holds 15 pupils.
How many rows are needed for 375 pupils?

I   1. 5 people are needed to make a sports team.
How many teams can be made from 17 people?

  2. 4 people can ride in a taxi.
Sam's class has 23 pupils.
How many taxis are needed for Sam's class?

Shopping...

What notes could you use to pay for these?
Is there more than one way?

Decimal point

There are 100 pence in a pound.

One pound is written as £1.00.

The dot between the pounds and pence is called a **decimal point**

Examples 6 pounds is written as £6.00.

Sometimes we just write £6.

3 pounds and 60 pence is written as £3.60.

45 pounds and 53 pence is written as £45.53.

23 pounds and 6 pence is written as £23.06.

56 pence is written as £0.56.

Exercise 1   Write these using £ and a decimal point.

1. 4 pounds
2. 7 pounds
3. 5 pounds and 69 pence
4. 2 pounds and 17 pence
5. 63 pounds and 40 pence
6. 18 pounds and 50 pence
7. 6 pounds and 50 pence
8. 43 pounds and 80 pence
9. 17 pounds and 6 pence
10. 24 pounds and 1 penny
11. 2 pounds and 8 pence
12. 36 pounds and 4 pence
13. 75 pence
14. 86 pence
15. 14 pence
16. 9 pence

Examples   £4.72 is 400 pence plus 72 pence.
£4.72 is 472 pence.

£8.09 is 800 pence plus 9 pence.
£8.09 is 809 pence.

£4.72

Exercise 2   Change these to pence.

1. £5.83
2. £6.50
3. £8.21
4. £3.40
5. £5.01
6. £3.09
7. £2.04
8. £0.85
9. £3
10. £0.65
11. £5

Sometimes we write **pence** as **p**.
So 153 pence is 153 p.
153 p is £1.53.

Exercise 3   Write these using £ and a decimal point.

1. 149 p
2. 256 p
3. 321 p
4. 640 p
5. 520 p
6. 360 p
7. 405 p
8. 201 p
9. 709 p
10. 604 p
11. 53 p
12. 79 p
13. 64 p
14. 802 p
15. 99 p

Example   Dai bought a lolly.
What coins could he use to pay for this?

20 p

Answer   He could use a 20 p coin
or two 10 p coins
or four 5 p coins
or a 10 p coin and two 5 p coins.

Are there other ways Dai could pay for this?

Exercise 4   Nina had these coins in her pocket.

Write down 2 ways that she could pay for these.

1.

40 p

2.

25 p

3.

50 p

4.

34 p

5.

45 p

6.

69 p

Example

Jan has these coins in her pocket. She has £1.45.

Exercise 5

How much money have each of these got?

1. Sally

one 20p　　two 10p　　four 2p

2. Ben

one £1　　one 50p　　one 20p

3. Aled

two 20p　　one 50p　　one 10p

4. Sudi

five 2p　　five 10p

5. Penny

seven 5p　　five 2p　　one 10p

6. Owen

two £1　　three 20p

five 10p　　six 5p

7. Pat

six 2p

four 20p

five 10p　　four 5p

8. Dan

four 20p　　three 10p　　eight 2p

9. Ann

three 50p　　five 20p　　three 5p　　seven 10p　　two 2p

Sometimes **change** has to be given.

Example   Brenda bought a Walnut Whip.
She paid with a £1 coin.

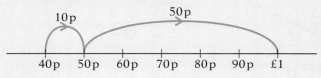 

40p

To give change, we need a 10 p coin to get to 50 p,
then a 50 p coin to get to £1.
So she got 60 p change.

Example   Sam paid for a 55 p chocolate bar with a £1 coin.
How much change will he get?

Answer

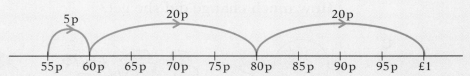

To give change we need a 5 p coin to get to 60 p and then two
20 p coins to get to £1.
Sam got 45 p change.

Exercise 6   **A**

1. Rob played a game of THROW.
    He paid with a £1 coin.
    How much change did he get?

2. Mary went for a ride on the motor bike.
    She paid with a £1 coin.
    How much change did she get?

3. Sue bought a toffee apple.
    She paid with a £1 coin.
    How much change did she get?

B

1.   Rob bought an exercise book. He gave 50 p.
     How much change did he get?

2.   Mary bought a pen. She gave £1.
     How much change did she get?

3.   Sue bought a ruler. She gave £1.
     How much change did she get?

C

Hats
£4.60

Suncream
£5.75

Flip-flops
£5.65

1.   Rob bought some suncream.
     He paid with six £1 coins.
     How much change should he get?

2.   Mary bought a hat.
     She paid with a £5 note.
     How much change should she get?

3.   Sue bought some flip flops.
     She paid with six £1 coins.
     How much change should she get?

Puzzle

Rob has 10 coins in his pocket.
They make £2.50.

Try and work out what they are.
Is there more than one answer?

Homework/Review 1

A Write these using £ and a decimal point.

1. 6 pounds
2. 5 pounds and 12 pence
3. 14 pounds and 60 pence
4. 29 pounds and 37 pence
5. 3 pounds and 6 pence
6. 14 pounds and 1 penny
7. 53 pence

B

| 105 p | 150 p | 155 p | 160 p | 165 p |

Fill in the gaps.
Choose from the box.

1. £1.65 is _____.
2. £1.60 is _____.
3. £1.50 is _____.
4. £1.05 is _____.
5. £1.55 is _____.

C Pip had these coins.

one 50p

three 20p

two 10p

five 5p

five 2p

Write down 2 ways that she could pay for these.

1.  60 p

2.  75 p

3.  £1.20

D How much money has Ken got?

one £1

four 5p

three 20p

three 2p

two 50p

E 1. Lisa gave a 50 p coin to pay for a 35 p Time Out bar.
How much change did she get?

2. Ken gave a £1 coin to pay for a 65 p cake.
How much change did he get?

Money on the calculator

£4.56 is shown on the calculator as ⟦ 4.56 ⟧

£7.08 is shown on the calculator as ⟦ 7.08 ⟧

£3.60 is shown on the calculator as ⟦ 3.6 ⟧

Exercise 7   Write down the letter of the calculator screen that shows these amounts of money.
  1. is shown by **D**.

  1. £4.45   2. £4.50   3. £4.05

  4. £4.40   5. £4.55   6. £4.04

  A ⟦ 4.4 ⟧   B ⟦ 4.5 ⟧   C ⟦ 4.55 ⟧

  D ⟦ 4.45 ⟧   E ⟦ 4.04 ⟧   F ⟦ 4.05 ⟧

+, −, ×, ÷ with money

We often need to do sums with money.

Example   Find the answer to £8.05 + £0.65.

Answer   Press 8 · 0 5 + 0 · 6 5 = to get ⟦ 8.7 ⟧
The answer is £8.70.
Could we press just 8 · 0 5 + · 6 5 = ?

Example   Find the answer to £42.48 ÷ 8.

Answer   Press 4 2 · 4 8 ÷ 8 = to get ⟦ 5.31 ⟧
The answer is £5.31.

Example Find the answer to £20 – £15.75.

Answer Press **2** **0** **–** **1** **5** **·** **7** **5** **=** to get `4.25`
The answer is £4.25.

Exercise 8 Find the answers to these.

1. £6.50 + £3.20   2. £7.15 + £4.75   3. £4.40 + £0.84
4. £5.42 × 4   5. £11.28 × 9   6. £3.05 × 15
7. £5 – £3.74   8. £15 – £12.05   9. £20.50 – £14.72
10. £49.80 ÷ 6   11. £56.40 ÷ 4   12. £43.96 ÷ 14
13. £2.70 × 7   14. £12.70 – £3.75   15. £70.40 ÷ 11
16. £4.91 + £0.63   17. £72.80 ÷ 13

Example Find the answer, in pounds, to 87 p × 12 in pounds.
Answer We write the 87 p as £0.87.

Press **0** **·** **8** **7** **×** **1** **2** **=** to get `10.44`
The answer is £10.44.

Exercise 9 Find the answer to these in pounds.

1. 64 p × 11   2. 46 p + £6.41   3. £10.50 – 32 p
4. £6.40 – 68 p   5. £10 – 59 p   6. 96 p × 7
7. £4.70 + 85 p   8. 87 p × 4   9. £20 – 68 p
10. 73 p × 12   11. £3.08 + 96 p

Exercise 10

| £6.35 | £11.17 | £5.63 | £8.60 |
| £6.04 | £3.68 | £8.06 | £13.41 |

1. ☐ + ☐ = £14.41
Which two amounts from the box make this true?

2. ☐ – ☐ = £7.78
Which two amounts from the box make this true?

Example   Pam had dinner.
It cost £16.45.
She paid with a £20 note.
How much change will she get?

Dinner
£16.45

Answer   We press ▢2 ▢0 ▢− ▢1 ▢6 ▢· ▢4 ▢5 ▢= to get   3.55

She got £3.55 change.

Exercise 11   A   1.   Ray bought lunch.
He paid with a £10 note.
How much change should he get?

2.   Tom bought lunch.
He paid with a £20 note.
How much change should he get?

TODAY
LUNCH
£5.60

B

CAKES

Plain   £1.80

Cream   £2.20

1.   Ray bought a plain cake.
He paid with a £5 note.
How much change should he get?

2.   Tom bought a cream cake.
He paid with a £10 note.
How much change should he get?

C   1.   Ray went to the movies.
He paid with a £5 note.
How much change should he get?

2.   Tom went to the movies.
He paid with a £10 note.
How much change should he get?

TODAY'S
MOVIE
£4.20

TILL 5PM

Example

RITA'S CAFE

Burger	£2.70
Pizza	£3.25
Chips	£0.80
Cola	£0.89

Jean bought pizza and cola.
1. How much did it cost?
2. How much change should she get from £5?

Answer 1. Pizza costs £3.25 and cola costs £0.89.
We must add £3.25 and £0.89.
We press

$\boxed{3}\ \boxed{\cdot}\ \boxed{2}\ \boxed{5}\ \boxed{+}\ \boxed{0}\ \boxed{\cdot}\ \boxed{8}\ \boxed{9}\ \boxed{=}$ to get $\boxed{4.14}$

It cost £4.14.

2. We must take away £4.14 from £5.
We press $\boxed{5}\ \boxed{-}\ \boxed{4}\ \boxed{\cdot}\ \boxed{1}\ \boxed{4}\ \boxed{=}$ to get $\boxed{0.86}$
She should get 86 p change.

Exercise 12   **A** Penny bought a burger from Rita's Cafe.
1. How much did it cost?
2. How much change should she get from £20?

B Nick bought a burger and cola.
1. How much did it cost?
2. How much change should he get from £10?

C Tai bought chips and cola.
1. How much did it cost?
2. How much change should he get from £2?

Example   Jacob bought 11 tickets to the disco.
How much did he pay altogether?

Answer   Press **2** **·** **2** **5** **×** **1** **1** **=**

to get $\boxed{24.75}$

The answer is £24.75.

DISCO
£2.25

Example   A group of friends went to the disco.
It cost them £18 altogether.
How many were in the group?

Answer   We must divide £18 by £2.25.

Press **1** **8** **÷** **2** **·** **2** **5** **=** to get $\boxed{8.}$

The answer is 8 people.

Exercise 13

A 1. A group of 13 went skating.
How much did they pay altogether?

2. Another group of 16 went skating.
How much did they pay altogether?

3. The group of 16 all bought morning tea.
How much did they pay for this?

B 1. A group of friends went skating.
They paid £33.60 altogether.
How many were in the group?

2. Another group of friends went skating.
They paid £50.40 altogether.
How many were in this group?

3. One group bought afternoon tea.
It cost £27.60 altogether.
How many were in this group?

Homework/Review 2

A Use a copy of this.
Write the amount next to the calculator screen.
The first one is done.

1. `7.06` £7.06   2. `7.6` _____

3. `6.07` _____   4. `6.7` _____

B **Can you spell COW in thirteen letters?**

Use a copy of this box.

L	£8.50 + £3.60 = £12.10
U	£5 – £2.40
S	£57.60 ÷ 9
B	£8.65 × 9
Y	£20 – £17.05
D	£6.80 + £0.80
O	£12.35 × 14
E	£189 ÷ 15

£6.40	£12.60	£12.60		£172.90

| | | | | L | |
| £7.60 | £172.90 | £2.60 | £77.85 | £12.10 | £12.60 |

£2.95	£172.90	£2.60

C 1. Rita bought a ticket.
She paid with a £20 note.
How much change should she get?

WILDLIFE PARK

Ticket   £12.50
Lunch   £8.60

2. Les bought a ticket and lunch.
How much did this cost altogether?

3. Ann bought 3 tickets.
She paid with a £50 note.
How much change should she get?

4. A group of 9 friends had lunch at the park.
How much did this lunch cost altogether?

5. Another group had lunch at the park.
It cost £111.80.
How many were in this group?

Game for 2 players: FIRST TO £50

You will need
- a dice
- the board below
- a pencil and paper
- a red counter and a blue counter
- a calculator

To play
- Put both counters on START.
- Take turns to roll the dice.
- Move the number of squares shown.
- Start with £0 and do what it says on the square.
- The winner is the first to get £50 or more.

START £0	+ £4.60	+ £4.20	+ £5.70	+ £3.80	+ £6.30
+ £1.60	+ 72p	× by 2	+ £1.50	+ £5.90	× by 2
+ £7.50	+ £0.90	− 80p	+ £4.60	− £3.80	+ £5.90
− £1.60	+ £3.70	− £0.80	+ 87p	+ 52p	− 68p
÷ by 2	+ £3.60	− £4.70	+ £8.90	£1.40	+ £4.30
+ £5.20	− £1.20	− £2.40	− £3.60	+ 96p	− 57p

◄◄ CHAPTER REVIEW ◄◄

◄◄
Exercise 1
on page 210

A Write these using £ and a decimal point.
1. 3 pounds
2. 6 pounds and 54 pence
3. 24 pounds and seventy pence
4. 17 pounds and 9 pence

◄◄
Exercise 2
on page 210

B Change these to pence.
1. £4.81
2. £9.70
3. £5.04
4. £0.65

◄◄
Exercise 3
on page 210

C Write these using £ and a decimal point.
1. 564 p
2. 205 p
3. 530 p
4. 85 p

◄◄
Exercises 4
and 5
on pages 211
and 212

D Lee has these coins in her pocket.

one £1   four 20p   six 10p   three 5p

1. How much money is this?
2. Write down 4 ways Lee could pay for this comic.

◄◄
Exercise 6
on page 213

E Lee paid for the comic with the £1 coin. How much change did she get?

45 p

◄◄
Exercise 8
and 9
on pages 217

F Find the answer to these.
1. £7.20 + £5.35
2. £20 − £17.40
3. £5.70 × 6
4. £74.80 ÷ 11
5. £23.60 − £4.10
6. £11.26 + 72 p

◄◄
Exercises 11,
12 and 13
on pages 218,
219 and 220

G 1. Sam bought a t-shirt.
He paid with a £20 note.
How much change should he get?

2. Tina bought a t-shirt and a hat.
How much did this cost?

3. A group of 8 friends all bought hats.
How much did this cost altogether?

4. Another group all bought t-shirts.
It cost £76.80.
How many were in this group?

FUN PARK

t-shirts   £12.80
hats   £7.40

17 Bar Charts

Newspapers

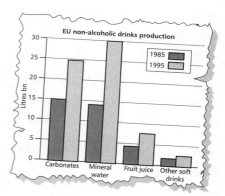

We often see charts in the paper.
Find as many as you can.
Make a poster of them.

Bar charts

Remember . . .

This is a **tally chart**.
‖ is 2.
卌 is 5.

Eye colour	Tally
brown	卌 ‖
blue	卌
grey	‖‖
green	‖

We can make a **block graph** from the tally chart.

Each block stands for one person.

How many people have brown eyes?
How many people have green eyes?

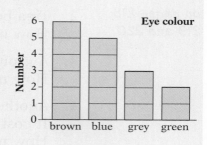

This is a **bar chart**.
It shows how Amy's
class came to school.

4 biked.
7 walked.
10 came by bus.
5 came by train.
2 came by car.

How many are there
in Amy's class?

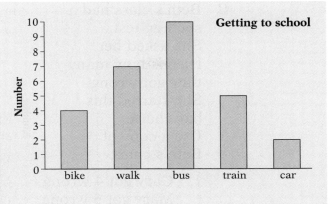

Getting to school

Exercise 1

A Beth had 5 dogs.
They all had puppies.

1. How many
   puppies did
   Candy have?
2. How many
   puppies did
   Nan have?
3. Which dog had
   the most puppies?
4. How many
   puppies did
   Beth's dogs
   have altogether?

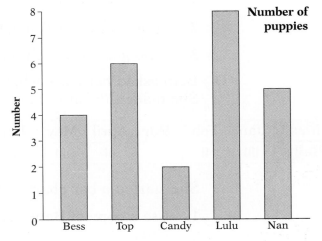

Number of puppies

B Beth played hockey.
This bar chart shows
the number of goals
scored by her team.

1. How many goals
   did Beth's team
   score in week 1?
2. Which week did
   they score no
   goals?
3. Which week did
   they score the
   most goals?

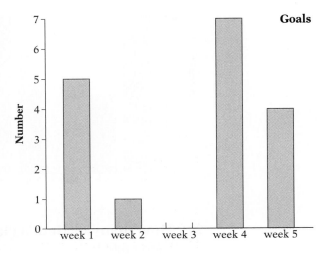

Goals

C Beth's class had a spelling test. She asked her friends how many they got wrong. She started this bar chart. Use a copy of Beth's chart.

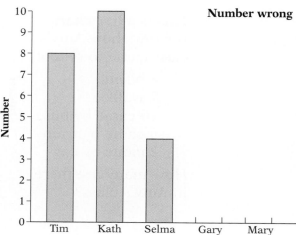

1. Gary got 4 wrong. Mary got 6 wrong. Draw the bars for Gary and Mary.

2. How many did Tim get wrong?

3. Who got the same number wrong as Gary?

D Beth asked her class what month they were born. She made this tally chart.

Month	Jan	Feb	Mar	April	May	Jun	Jul	Aug	Sept	Oct	Nov	Dec
Tally	IIII	II		III	IIII	I	I	III	LHT	II	IIII	I

She started a bar chart.

1. Use a copy of Beth's chart. Finish it.

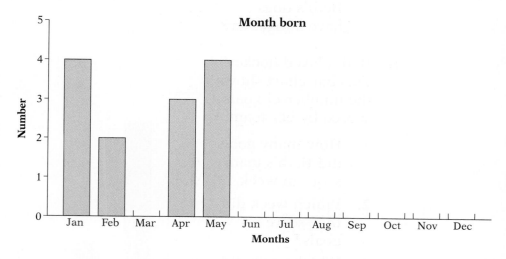

2. How many of Beth's class have birthdays in the first half of the year?

Sometimes the numbers up the side don't go up in ones.

Example

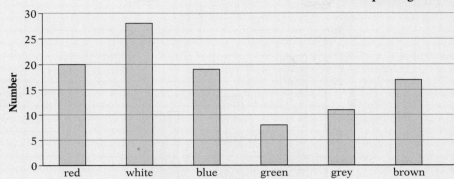

Cars passing school

The numbers on this bar chart go up in fives.
Look at the top of the bar for white cars.

The top of this bar is at 28.
There were **28** white cars.

How many grey cars were there?
How many brown cars were there?

Exercise 2   **A**   Sam's school had a sports
day with other schools.
Sam started this chart to
show how his school did.

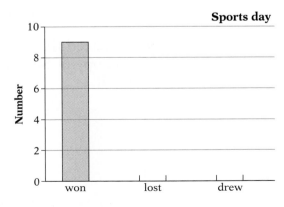

Sports day

They lost 4 times.
They drew 7 times.

1. How many games
    did they win?
2. Use a copy of
    Sam's chart.
    Draw the bars for lost and drew.
3. How many games did they play altogether?

B   Sam's class made things for a sales table at sports day.
Sam started this bar chart of what they sold.
Use a copy of Sam's bar chart.

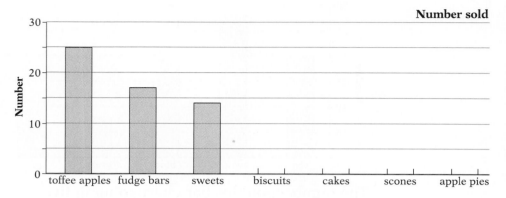

Number sold

1.   They sold 29 biscuits
                19 cakes
                23 scones
                17 apple pies.
Draw the bars for these on your bar chart.
2.   How many fudge bars did they sell?
3.   How many sweets did they sell?
4.   What did they sell most of?
5.   Toffee apples cost 80 p each.
How much did they make on these altogether?

C   The tuck shop was open on sports day.
This tally chart shows what was bought.

fruit	crisps	drink	bars	soup	rolls
ЦНТ ЦНТ ЦНТ ЦНТ ЦНТ ЦНТ	ЦНТ ЦНТ ЦНТ ЦНТ ЦНТ III	ЦНТ ЦНТ ЦНТ ЦНТ ЦНТ IIII	ЦНТ ЦНТ ЦНТ ЦНТ III	ЦНТ ЦНТ ЦНТ II	ЦНТ ЦНТ ЦНТ I

Sam started this bar chart.
Use a copy of Sam's chart.
Finish it.

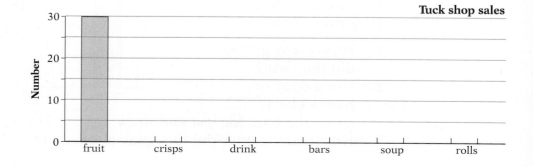

Tuck shop sales

Exercise 3

Colin wrote down how long he watched TV for each week.
He started to draw this bar chart.

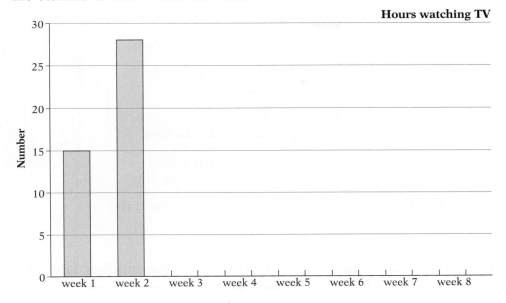

Hours watching TV

He watched 10 hours in week 4
16 hours in week 5
0 hours in week 6
11 hours in week 7
23 hours in week 8.

1. Use a copy of Colin's bar chart.
    Finish it.

2. One week Colin went on a hiking holiday.
    Which week do you think this was?

3. One week Colin had a lot of homework.
    Which week do you think this was?

4. Colin likes watching sport on TV.
    Which two weeks do you think there was a lot of sport on TV?

Sometimes bar charts have the bars touching.

Example   This bar chart shows the number late for school.

Which of these sentences is true?

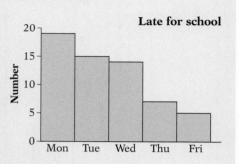

Late for school

A   Each day there were more late than the day before.

B   Each day there were not as many late as the day before.

C   The number of pupils late was about the same each day.

Answer   The bars are getting lower each day. So **B** is true.

Exercise 4

A   Samira's class wrote down the number late each day for 3 weeks. Which bar chart matches these sentences?

1.   The number of pupils late was about the same each day.

2.   There were no pupils late one day this week.

3.   Each day there were more pupils late than the day before.

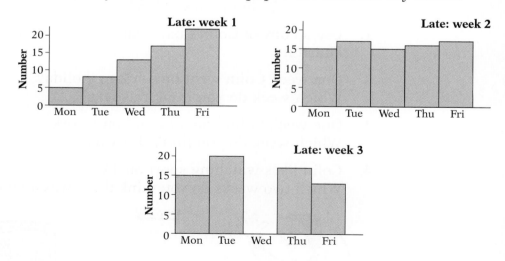

B   Look at the bar charts for late pupils in **A**. What number goes in the gap?

1.   There was a school trip one day in week _____.

2.   The weather got colder and colder in week _____.

Homework/Review

A Huda asked her friends what they thought of The Spice Girls.

She started to draw this bar chart. Use a copy of Huda's chart.

Spice Girls

1. 4 people didn't like them much.
   2 people didn't like them at all.
   Draw these bars on your chart.
2. How many liked them lots?
3. How many friends did Huda ask?

B Ben wrote down how many minutes homework he did each night.

He started to draw this bar chart.

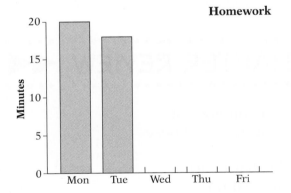

Homework

1. How many minutes did he do on Monday?
2. How many minutes did he do on Tuesday?
3. Ben did 15 minutes on Wednesday
          4 minutes on Thursday
         12 minutes on Friday.
   Use a copy of Ben's chart.
   Draw on the bars for Wednesday, Thursday and Friday.
4. Ben started his homework one night.
   Then he found he had forgotten his book.
   Which night do you think this was?

Task

1. Choose one of these questions.

    How many people were late each day last week?
    Which of these do you like best?

    fudge   chocolate bars   candy floss

    Which of these do you like best?

    Fanta   Coke   lemonade   juice   water

    What flavour crisps do you like best?

    What TV show do you like best?

    How many bits of rubbish are left after lunch each day?

    How many people go the library each lunchtime?

    You can make up a different question if you want to.

2. Make up a collection sheet for the answers.

3. Draw a bar chart.

◄◄ CHAPTER REVIEW ◄◄

◄◄
Exercise 1
on page 225

A Jon counted the number of buses that went past his house each night.
He started this bar chart.
11 buses went past on Thursday and 12 on Friday.

1. Use a copy of Jon's chart. Draw on the bars for Thursday and Friday.

2. How many buses went past on Monday?

3. How many went past on Tuesday?

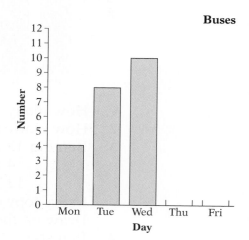

◀◀
Exercise 2
on page 227

B Gareth asked his friends
how many comics they
read last month.
He started this bar chart.
   Huw read 8
   Ed read 13
   Joe read 11

Use a copy of Gareth's chart.

1. Draw the bars for Huw,
    Ed and Joe on your chart.

2. How many comics did Jon
    read?

3. Who read the most comics?

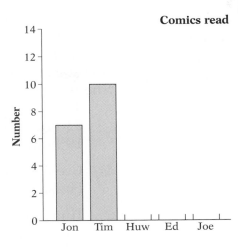

Comics read

◀◀
Exercise 2
on page 227

C Huda had some tests.
She started this bar chart to
show her marks.

Use a copy of Huda's chart.

1. Huda got 38 in History

    She got 43 in Science.

    Draw these bars on
    your chart.

2. What did Huda
    get in French?

3. What did Huda do best in?

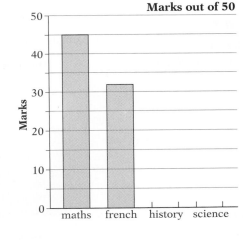

Marks out of 50

◀◀

Exercises 3
and 4
on pages 229
and 230

D Tina likes to be outside.
She wrote down how many hours
she spent outside each week.
She started to draw this bar chart.
She was outside for
    4 hours in week 4
    23 hours in week 5
    19 hours in week 6.

1. Use a copy of Tina's chart.
   Finish it.

2. Tina was sick for most of
   one week.
   Which week do you think this was?

3. The weather was fine every day one week.
   Which week do you think this was?

◀◀

Exercise 4
on page 230

E Mrs. Brown is a taxi driver.
She wrote down how far she drove each day for 3 weeks.

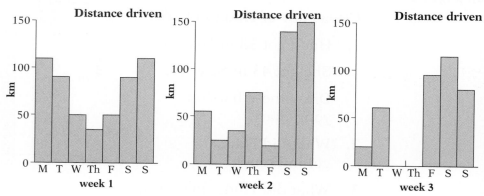

Which bar chart matches these sentences?

1. Mrs. Brown didn't drive at all on 2 days this week.

2. Mrs. Brown drove most at the beginning and end of the week.

3. Mrs. Brown drove a lot on 2 days and not so much on 5 days.

◀◀

Exercise 4
on page 230

F Look at the bar charts in **E**.
What number goes in the gap?

1. Mrs. Brown was sick for 2 days in week _____.

2. There was a bus strike on in the weekend of week _____.

18 Patterns

At school

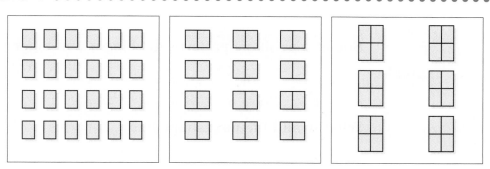

These are patterns made with desks.
Draw some more desk patterns.
What other patterns can you find at school?
Think about these.
  • classrooms   • trees   • windows   • the gym

Shape patterns

This is a **shape pattern**. □ △ ○ □ △ ○ □ △ ○

The next shape would be □

How can we tell?
What would the next shape after that be?

Exercise 1   Draw the next 3 shapes of these patterns.

1. ⬤ □ ☆ ⬤ □ ☆   2. ∘ ⬭ ◯ ∘ ⬭ ◯ ∘

3. △ ∘ ▭ △ ∘ ▭ △ ∘   4. □ △ ○ ▮ □ △ ○ ▮ □ △

5. **P B C S P B C S P B**   6. / □ S ∘ / □ S ∘ /

7. □ ▵ □ ▵▵ □ ▵ □ ▵▵ □   8. ∘ ⬭ ∘∘ ⬭ ∘ ⬭ ∘∘ ⬭

9. △ ○ ○ △ ○ △ ○ ○   10. ○△○○△○○○△○○○○△○○○

11. □ ∘ □ □ ∘∘ □ ∘ □ □ ∘∘   12. ☆◁☆☆◁◁☆◁☆☆◁◁

13. ⊕⊕⊕⊕⊕⊕⊕⊕   14. ⊕⊕⊕⊕⊕⊕⊕⊕

15. ● ○ ○ ● ○ ○ ○ ● ○ ○ ○

Sometimes shape patterns get bigger and bigger.

Example

What would the next shape be?

Exercise 2   Draw the next shape.

1. △   △△   △△△   △△△△

2. Y   YY   YYY

3. ⊟   ⊟⊟   ⊟⊟⊟

4. ◇⁺   ◇⁺◇⁺   ◇⁺◇⁺◇⁺

5. △   △▽   △▽△

6. ∟   ∟∟   ∟∟∟

7. ⟨   ⟨⟩   ⟨⟩⟨

Puzzle   Use a copy of this. Find the missing shapes.

1.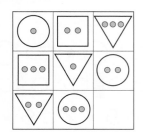

2.

3.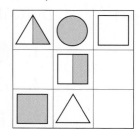

Task

You will need   some matches
some counters of different colours
some blocks like multilink cubes or Lego

A   Make some patterns using matches.
Here are some ideas.

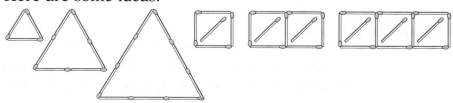

Explain how your patterns are made.

B   Make some patterns with counters.
Here are some ideas.

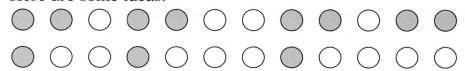

Explain how your patterns are made.

C   Make some patterns with blocks.

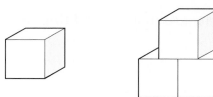
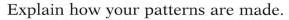
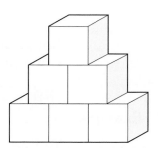

Explain how your patterns are made.

Number patterns

These are **number patterns**.
1, 2, 1, 2, 1, 2, 1, 2, ...
1, 1, 2, 1, 1, 2, 1, 1, 2, ...
1, 2, 1, 1, 2, 2, 1, 1, 1, 2, 2, 2, ...
What do you think the ... at the end means?

Exercise 3   What might the next 3 numbers be?
1.   3, 4, 3, 4, 3, 4, 3, ...
2.   3, 3, 4, 4, 3, 3, 4, 4, ...
3.   1, 2, 2, 1, 2, 2, 1, 2, 2, ...
4.   1, 2, 1, 1, 2, 2, 1, 1, 1, 2, 2, 2, 1, 1, ...
5.   10, 9, 8, 9, 10, 9, 8, 9, ...
6.   2, 1, 2, 2, 1, 1, 2, 2, 2, 1, 1, 1, 2, 2, ...

Remember . . .

The **odd** numbers are 1, 3, 5, 7, 9, 11, 13 and so on.
The **even** numbers are 2, 4, 6, 8, 10, 12, 14 and so on.

The odd numbers make a number pattern.
So do the even numbers.

Exercise 4   What numbers go in the gaps?
1.   1, 3, 5, 7, 9, ___, 13   2.   2, 4, 6, 8, ___, 12, 14
3.   9, 11, 13, ___, 17   4.   10, 12, ___, 16, 18
5.   5, 7, ___, 11, 13 ___, 17   6.   6, ___, ___, 12, 14, ___, 18
7.   ___, 18, ___, 22, ___, 26

Some number patterns are made by adding or subtracting the same number.

Example
+3 +3 +3 +3
3,   6,   9,   12,   15, ...

To find the next 2 numbers, we keep adding 3.

+3 +3
3,   6,   9,   12,   15,   18,   21

Example
−2 −2 −2 −2
20,   18,   16,   14,   12, ...

To find the next 2 numbers, we keep subtracting 2.

−2 −2
20,   18,   16,   14,   12,   10,   8

Exercise 5   Use a copy of this.
Fill in the boxes.
The first one has been done.

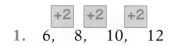

1. 6,   8,   10,   12

2. 1,   4,   7,   10,   13

3. 16,   14,   12,   10

4. 18,   15,   12,   9

5. 0,   4,   8,   12,   16

6. 5,   10,   15,   20,   25

7. 3,   7,   11,   15

Exercise 6   Write down the next 3 numbers.

1. 6, 8, 10, 12, ...   **2.** 1, 4, 7, 10, 13, ...
3. 16, 14, 12, 10, ...   **4.** 18, 15, 12, 9, ...
5. 0, 4, 8, 12, 16, ... **6.** 5, 10, 15, 20, 25, ...

Exercise 7   What number goes in the box?

1. 2, 4, ☐, 8, 10, ...   **2.** 3, 6, 9, ☐, 15, ...
3. 5, ☐, 15, 20, ...   **4.** 4, 8, 12, ☐, 20, ...
5. 20, 15, ☐, 5, ...   **6.** 21, 18, 15, 12, ☐, 6, ...
7. 2, 6, 10, ☐, 18, ...   **8.** 20, 16, 12, ☐, 4, ...
9. 1, 6, 11, 16, ☐, 26, ...

Exercise 8

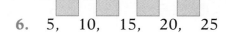

1. What will be above 10?
2. What will be above 11?
3. What will be above 13?
4. What will be above 20?
5. Will ⊗ be above 30?
6. What will be above 25?

Investigation

You will need four piles of different colour counters (you need about 10 in each pile) a strip of paper like this, 30cm long.

1	2	3	4	5	6	7	8	9	10	...
										...

Have your numbers go up to about 20.

Put one counter of each colour on squares 1, 2, 3, 4.
Make this pattern over and over along the strip.

1	2	3	4	5	6	7	8	9	10	11	12	13	14	15	...
⚪	🔘	⚫	⚪	⚪	🔘	⚫	⚪	⚪	🔘	⚫	⚪	⚪	🔘	⚫	

Example   Choose one colour counter.
Write down the numbers above it.
Write down more numbers it would have if the strip was longer.
Do this for the other colours.

Now make a different pattern using 2, 3 or 4 colours.

1	2	3	4	5	6	7	8	9	10	11	12	13	14	15	...
🔘	🔘	⚪	🔘	🔘	⚪	🔘	🔘	⚪	🔘	🔘	⚪	🔘	🔘	⚪	

Example   Green has the number pattern 1, 2, 4, 5, 7, 8, 10, 11, 13, 14, ...
What number pattern does grey have?

Make some more patterns.
Write down the number pattern for each colour.

Homework/Review 1

A Draw the next 3 shapes of these patterns.

1.

2.

3.

4.

5.

6.

B Draw the next shape of these patterns.

1.

2.

3.

C **Why did Robin Hood steal from the rich?**
Use a copy of this.

	E					E			E
4	8	20	5	13	15	8	16	6	8

23	3	3	50	1	12	1	10	16

			E			
6	5	25	8	5	10	2

			E	
18	3	10	8	2

What number goes in the box?

E 2, 4, 6, 8, 10, 12, ...
A ☐, 7, 9, 11, 13, ...
I 3, 6, 9, ☐, ...
B 12, 10, 8, 6, ☐, ...
S 5, 10, ☐, 20, ...
T 10, 12, 14, ☐, 18, ...
U 1, 4, 7, 10, ☐, 16, ...
H 15, 12, 9, ☐, 3, ...
Y 14, 10, 6, ☐, ...

C 0, 4, 8, 12, 16, ☐, ...
V 10, 15, 20, ☐, ...
N 25, 20, 15, ☐, 5, ...
D 1, 1, 2, 1, 1, 2, 1, ☐, ...
O 3, 4, 3, 3, 4, 4, ☐, 3, 3, 4, 4, 4, ...
R 10, 20, 30, 40, ☐, 60, ...
M 2, 6, 10, 14, ☐, 22, ...
P 3, 8, 13, 18, ☐, 28, ...

Addition and subtraction patterns

This is an addition pattern. $6 + 0 = 6$
The numbers in the first box are one less each time. $5 + 1 = 6$
The numbers in the next box are one more each time. $4 + 2 = 6$
What would the next line of the pattern be? $3 + 3 = 6$

Exercise 9   Write down the next 2 lines of these patterns.

1. $5 + 0 = 5$
    $4 + 1 = 5$
    $3 + 2 = 5$

2. $8 + 0 = 8$
    $7 + 1 = 8$
    $6 + 2 = 8$

3. $0 + 10 = 10$
    $1 + \ 9 = 10$
    $2 + \ 8 = 10$

4. $5 + 4 = 9$
    $6 + 3 = 9$
    $7 + 2 = 9$

5. $8 - 4 = 4$
    $7 - 3 = 4$
    $6 - 2 = 4$

6. $9 - 6 = 3$
    $8 - 5 = 3$
    $7 - 4 = 3$

7. $5 + 0 = 5$
    $5 + 1 = 6$
    $5 + 2 = 7$

8. $8 - 4 = 4$
    $8 - 3 = 5$
    $8 - 2 = 6$

9. $9 - 5 = 4$
    $9 - 4 = 5$
    $9 - 3 = 6$

10. $10 + 4 = 14$
    $10 + 5 = 15$
    $10 + 6 = 16$

11. $9 + 5 = 14$
    $9 + 6 = 15$
    $9 + 7 = 16$

12. $15 - 7 = 8$
    $15 - 8 = 7$
    $15 - 9 = 6$

Exercise 10   Make a copy of this.

_____ + _____ = 10

_____ + _____ = 10

_____ + _____ = 10

_____ + _____ = 10

Fill in the gaps to make a pattern.
One way is $4 + 6 = 10$
$5 + 5 = 10$
$6 + 4 = 10$
$7 + 3 = 10$

How many ways can you find?

$$7 + 10 = \boxed{17}$$
$$\boxed{17} + 10 = \boxed{27}$$
$$\boxed{27} + 10 = \boxed{37}$$
$$\boxed{37} + 10 = \boxed{47}$$

$$5 + 9 = \boxed{14}$$
$$\boxed{15} + 9 = \boxed{24}$$
$$\boxed{25} + 9 = \boxed{34}$$
$$\boxed{35} + 9 = \boxed{44}$$

$$6 + 8 = \boxed{14}$$
$$\boxed{16} + 8 = \boxed{24}$$
$$\boxed{26} + 8 = \boxed{34}$$
$$\boxed{36} + 8 = \boxed{44}$$

Look at the numbers in the boxes.
What is the pattern?
What would the next line of each be?

Exercise 11   Write down the next 2 lines of these patterns.

1. $4 + 10 = 14$
    $14 + 10 = 24$
    $24 + 10 = 34$

2. $8 + 10 = 18$
    $18 + 10 = 28$
    $28 + 10 = 38$

3. $4 + 6 = 10$
    $14 + 6 = 20$
    $24 + 6 = 30$

4. $8 + 7 = 15$
    $18 + 7 = 25$
    $28 + 7 = 35$

5. $16 - 10 = 6$
    $26 - 10 = 16$
    $36 - 10 = 26$

6. $9 - 4 = 5$
    $19 - 4 = 15$
    $29 - 4 = 25$

7. $16 - 7 = 9$
    $26 - 7 = 19$
    $36 - 7 = 29$

8. $9 + 8 = 17$
    $19 + 8 = 27$
    $29 + 8 = 37$

9. $15 - 9 = 6$
    $25 - 9 = 16$
    $35 - 9 = 26$

10. $9 + 6 = 15$
    $19 + 6 = 25$
    $29 + 6 = 35$

11. $19 - 12 = 7$
    $29 - 12 = 17$
    $39 - 12 = 27$

Investigation

$1 + 2 = 3$
$4 + 5 + 6 = 7 + 8$
$9 + 10 + 11 + 12 = 13 + 14 + 15$

Look at this pattern.
How has it been made?
Check the answers with your calculator.
Write down the next line of the pattern.
Check it with your calculator.
Keep writing down the next line and checking it.

Investigation

1	2	3	4	5	6	7	8	9	10
11	12	13	14	15	16	17	18	19	20
21	22	23	24	25	26	27	28	29	30

Write down as many number patterns as you can using these numbers and +, –, =

Homework/Review 2

A Write down the next 2 lines of these patterns.

1. $7 + 0 = 7$
    $6 + 1 = 7$
    $5 + 2 = 7$

2. $1 + 8 = 9$
    $2 + 7 = 9$
    $3 + 6 = 9$

3. $9 - 5 = 4$
    $8 - 4 = 4$
    $7 - 3 = 4$

4. $8 + 6 = 14$
    $8 + 7 = 15$
    $8 + 8 = 16$

5. $17 - 9 = 8$
    $17 - 10 = 7$
    $17 - 11 = 6$

B Write down the next 2 lines of these patterns.

1. $19 + 10 = 29$
    $29 + 10 = 39$
    $39 + 10 = 49$

2. $12 - 7 = 5$
    $22 - 7 = 15$
    $32 - 7 = 25$

3. $8 + 6 = 14$
    $18 + 6 = 24$
    $28 + 6 = 34$

C Make a copy of this.
Fill in the gaps to make a pattern.

1. $\underline{9} + \underline{\quad} = 14$

    $\underline{8} + \underline{\quad} = 14$

    $\underline{7} + \underline{7} = 14$

    $\underline{\quad} + \underline{\quad} = 14$

2. $\underline{14} - \underline{\quad} = 5$

    $\underline{15} - \underline{\quad} = 5$

    $\underline{16} - \underline{11} = 5$

    $\underline{\quad} - \underline{\quad} = 5$

Game for 1 player: JUMPS

You will need   blue counters

black counters

this board

To play   • Put the counters on the board like this.

• Take turns to move a black counter, then a green counter.

• You may move a counter one square

or you may jump over a counter of the other colour.

Example   At the start:

Black has moved one square.   Green has jumped over black.

• You have finished when the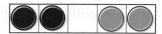
counters look like this.

• Now try this.

Begin like this.   End like this.

• Now try this.

Begin like this.

End like this

• Try even bigger ones.

◀◀ CHAPTER REVIEW ◀◀

◀◀
Exercise 1
on page 235

A Draw the next 3 shapes of these patterns.

1.

2.

3.

4.

◀◀
Exercise 2
on page 236

B Draw the next shape.

1.

2.

◀◀
Exercise 3
on page 238

C What might the next 3 numbers be?

1. 5, 6, 6, 5, 6, 6, 5, 6, 6, 5, ...
2. 1, 2, 3, 1, 1, 2, 2, 3, 3, 1, 1, 1, 2, ...

◀◀
Exercise 6
on page 239

D Write down the next 3 numbers.

1. 4, 6, 8, 10, 12, 14, ...   2. 3, 6, 9, 12, ...
3. 5, 10, 15, 20, ...   4. 1, 5, 9, 13, ...

◀◀
Exercise 7
on page 239

E What number goes in the box?

1. 5, ■, 9, 11, ...   2. 8, 10, 12, ■, 16, ...
3. 20, 18, 16, ■, 12, ...   4. 20, ■, 10, 5, ...

◀◀
Exercise 9
on page 242

F Write down the next 2 lines of these patterns.

1. $6 + 3 = 9$ 2. $7 - 5 = 2$ 3. $19 - 8 = 11$
    $5 + 4 = 9$ $6 - 4 = 2$ $19 - 9 = 10$
    $4 + 5 = 9$ $5 - 3 = 2$ $19 - 10 = 9$

◀◀
Exercise 11
on page 243

G Write down the next 2 lines of these patterns.

1. $7 + 8 = 15$ 2. $15 - 9 = 6$ 3. $19 - 11 = 8$
    $17 + 8 = 25$ $25 - 9 = 16$ $29 - 11 = 18$
    $27 + 8 = 35$ $35 - 9 = 26$ $39 - 11 = 28$

Quick Test 6

A

TOPP PARK

Adults: **Fifteen pounds and ninety five pence**

Children under 1 metre: **FREE!**

Group of 30 or more: **Nine pounds and fifty pence**

1. Write fifteen pounds and ninety five pence using £ and a decimal point.
2. Write £9.50 in pence.

B Jan has these in her pocket.

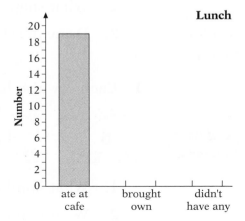

one £5   five £1   three 50p   four 20p   two 10p

1. How much money is this?
2. Write down a way Jan could pay £9.50 to get into Topp Park.

C Jill paid the £15.95 with a £20 note.
How much change did she get?

D Five friends went to Topp Park.
How much did this cost altogether?

E Another group all bought £15.95 tickets.
It cost £175.45.
How many were in the group?

F Topp Park asked some people about lunch.
This bar chart was started.
  15 brought their own lunch
  7 didn't have any
1. Use a copy of this bar chart. Draw on the bars for 'brought their own lunch' and 'didn't have any'.
2. How many ate lunch at the cafe?

G Topp Park counted how many people used the Log Ride in the first 10 minutes each day.

This bar chart was started.

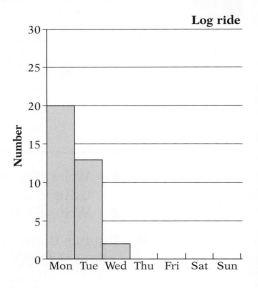

17 used it on Thursday

9 used it on Friday

28 used it on Saturday

22 used it on Sunday

1. Use a copy of this bar chart. Draw on the bars for Thursday, Friday, Saturday and Sunday.

2. How many people used it on Tuesday?

3. The weather was wet one day. Which day do you think this was?

H Each car in a ride has a shape on one side.

1. What shape goes on the green car?

2. Draw the shapes that will be on the next 3 cars you see.

I Each car also has a number.

1. What number goes on the green car?

2. What numbers will be on the next 2 cars you see?

More Measures

Getting smaller ....

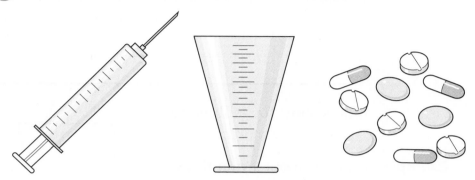

Doctors use small amounts.
Which of these people use small amounts?

- dentist
- teacher
- builder
- eye doctor
- gardener

Small measures

Remember . . .

We use these measures.

miles	pounds	pints
feet	kilograms kg	litres *l*
inches		
kilometres km		
metres m		
centimetres cm		

A ruler is divided into centimetres.
Each centimetre is divided into **millimetres**.

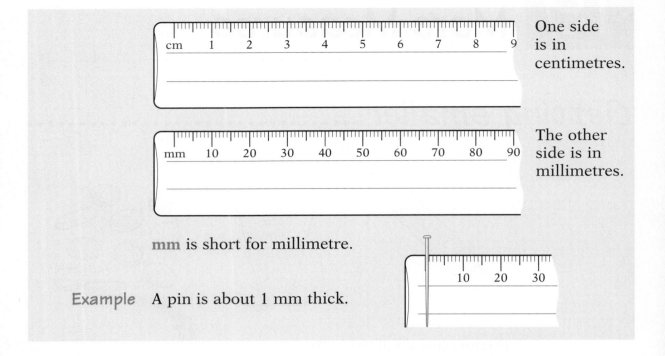

mm is short for millimetre.

Example   A pin is about 1 mm thick.

Exercise 1   Write down the letters of the things we measure in millimetres.

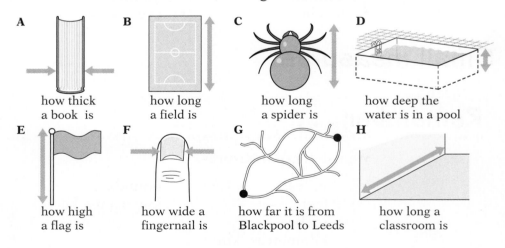

A   how thick a book is

B   how long a field is

C   how long a spider is

D   how deep the water is in a pool

E   how high a flag is

F   how wide a fingernail is

G   how far it is from Blackpool to Leeds

H   how long a classroom is

A litre is divided into **millilitres**.
m*l* is short for millilitres.
A teaspoon holds about 5 m*l*.
A cup holds about 200 m*l*.

Exercise 2   All of these hold water.

Write down the ones we would measure in millilitres.

cup	sink	coke bottle	bath
eggcup	teaspoon	bucket	small jug

A kilogram is divided into **grams**.
g is short for grams.
An apple weighs about 150 g.

Exercise 3   Write down the letters of the things we measure in grams.

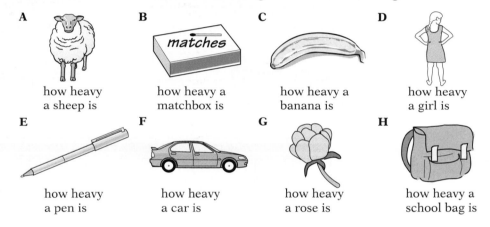

A   how heavy a sheep is

B   how heavy a matchbox is

C   how heavy a banana is

D   how heavy a girl is

E   how heavy a pen is

F   how heavy a car is

G   how heavy a rose is

H   how heavy a school bag is

Measuring in mm

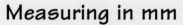

Each mark on this scale is 1 millimetre.

Examples

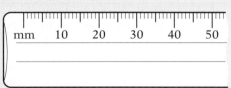

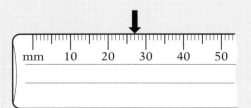

This arrow is pointing to 27 mm.

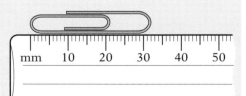

This paper clip is 32 mm long.

Exercise 4   **A**   What are these arrows pointing to?

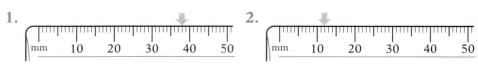

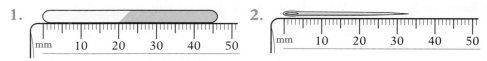

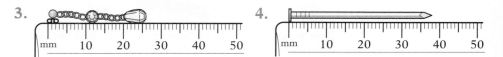

B   How long are these?

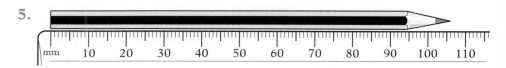

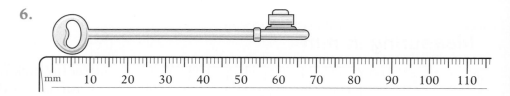

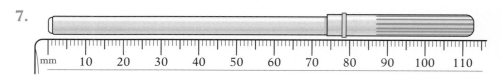

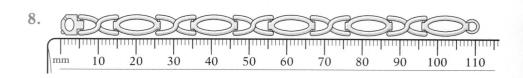

Measuring in grams

Each mark on this scale is 10 grams.
We count in tens.

Examples

This sugar weighs 120 grams.   These carrots weigh 380 grams.

Exercise 5   How much do these weigh?

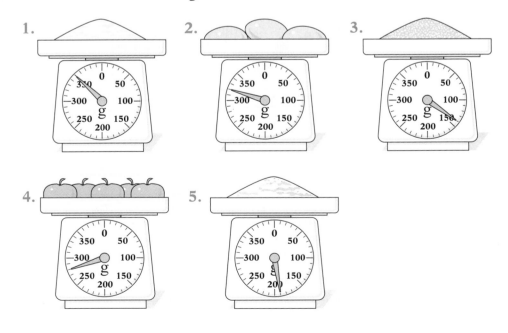

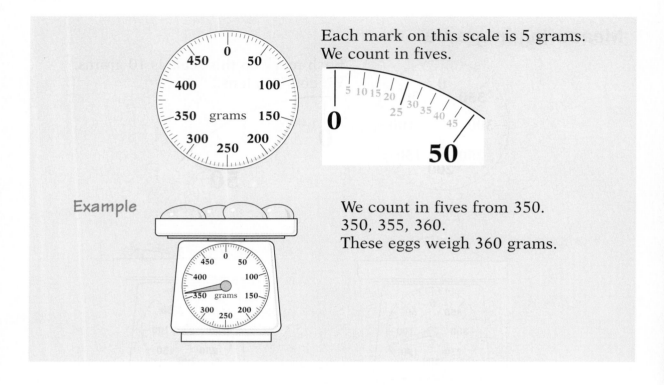

Each mark on this scale is 5 grams.
We count in fives.

Example

We count in fives from 350.
350, 355, 360.
These eggs weigh 360 grams.

Exercise 6   How much do these weigh?

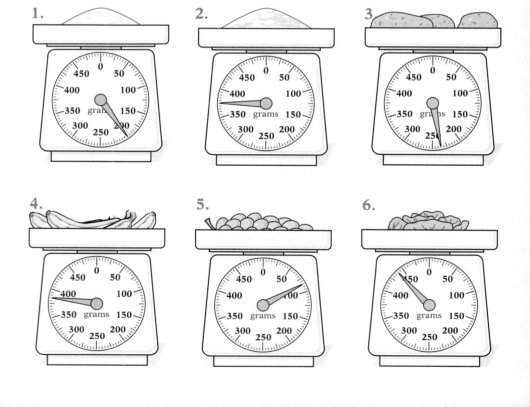

1.

2.

3.

4.

5.

6.

Measuring in ml

Each mark on this scale is 50 ml
We count in 50s.

Example

We count in 50s from 600.
600, 650, 700, 750.
This jug has 750 ml of milk in it.

Exercise 7   How much milk is in these jugs?

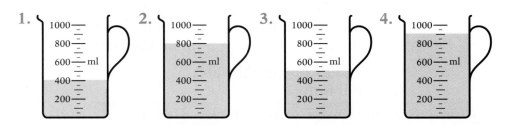

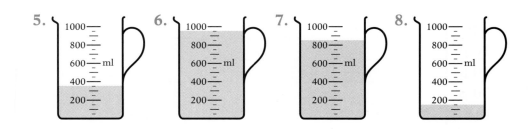

Task

A Draw around your hand.
Measure the length of each finger.
Do the same for your other hand.
Use a copy of this table.
Fill it in.

	Right hand	**Left hand**
1st finger	_____ mm	_____ mm
2nd finger	_____ mm	_____ mm
3rd finger	_____ mm	_____ mm
4th finger	_____ mm	_____ mm
thumb	_____ mm	_____ mm

Are your fingers the same length on both hands?

B You will need a packet of crisps, a packet of sweets and a packet of sugar.
Weigh what is inside each packet.
Did you get the same as the weight given on the packet?

C You will need some coins.
Measure each coin.

Measure across
the coin.

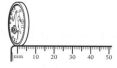

Measure how
thick the coin is.

Measure how much
the coin weighs.

Use a copy of this table.
Fill it in.

Coin	How far across	How thick	How heavy
1 p			
2 p			
5 p			
10 p			
20 p			
50 p			
£1			

Would you rather have
200 grams of 50 p coins
or 100 grams of £1 coins?

Homework/Review 1

A What goes in the gap?

1. m*l* is short for _____.
2. _____ is short for gram.
3. _____ is short for millimetre.

B **When is the moon heaviest?**

Use a copy of this box.
Match each scale with a number in the box.
The first one is done.

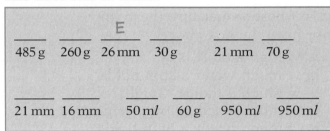

		E			
____	____	____	____	____	____
485 g	260 g	26 mm	30 g	21 mm	70 g
____	____	____	____	____	____
21 mm	16 mm	50 m*l*	60 g	950 m*l*	950 m*l*

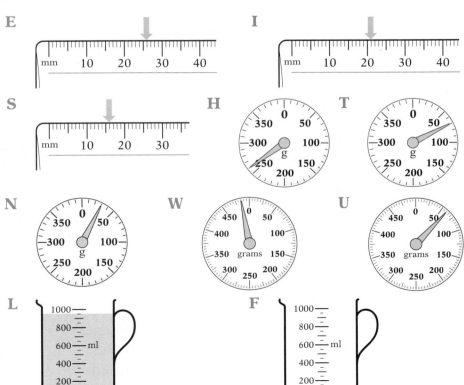

Choosing what to measure with

Check that you know all of the measures in the box.

km	m	cm	mm	mile	*l*	m*l*
	pint	kg	g	pound		

Example   It is best to measure how much a bag of potatoes weighs in kg or pounds.

Exercise 8

What is it best to measure these in?
Choose from the box above.

1. how high a table is
2. how much water a sink holds
3. how much a mouse weighs
4. how much a school bag weighs
5. how much water a bath holds
6. how much a cat weighs
7. how tall your teacher is
8. how much milk a glass holds
9. how long a wall is
10. how much a boy weighs
11. how wide a road is
12. how long a motorway is
13. how much water Tom drank today
14. how much a slice of cheese weighs

Exercise 9

What goes in the gap?
Choose from the box at the top of the page.

1. This book is about 18 _____ across.
2. A classroom is about 3 _____ high.
3. A pin is about 30 _____ long.
4. A glass holds about 150 _____ of water.
5. An apple weighs about 150 _____.
6. A desk is about 90 _____ high.
7. Jan is 11. She weighs about 40 _____.
8. Jon's mother had a baby today. It weighs about 7 _____.

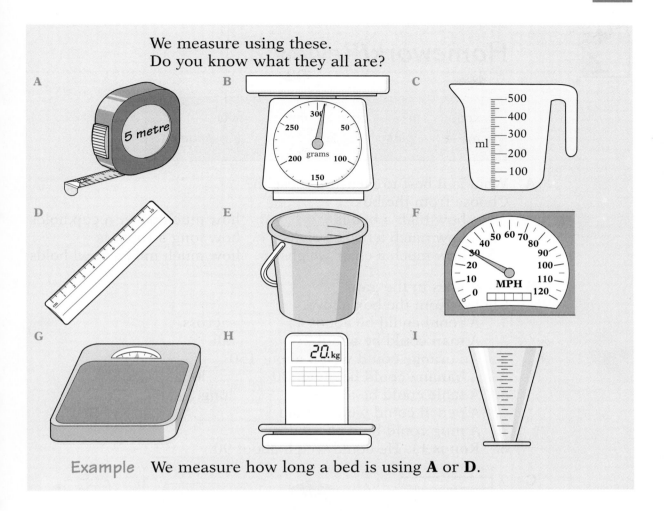

We measure using these.
Do you know what they all are?

A
B
C
D
E
F
G
H
I

Example   We measure how long a bed is using **A** or **D**.

Exercise 10   What would you use to measure these?

Choose from the pictures above.
1. how high a table is
2. how much water a sink holds
3. how much a mouse weighs
4. how much a school bag weighs
5. how much water a bath holds
6. how much a cat weighs
7. how tall your teacher is
8. how much milk a glass holds
9. how long a wall is
10. how much a boy weighs
11. how wide a road is
12. how long a motorway is
13. how much water Tom drank today

Homework/Review 2

km	m	cm	mm	mile	*l*
m*l*	pint	kg	g	pound	

A What is it best to measure these in?
Choose from the box.
1. how high a bed is
2. how much water a cup holds
3. how much a book weighs
4. how long a room is
5. how much a chair weighs
6. how much milk a bowl holds

B What goes in the gap?
Choose from the box above.
1. A room could be about 4 _____ across.
2. A man could be about 2 _____ tall.
3. An orange could weigh about 150 _____ .
4. A banana could be about 20 _____ long.
5. A table could be about 2 _____ long.
6. A pencil could weigh about 5 _____ .
7. A mug could hold about 200 _____ .
8. Ron is 11. He could weigh about 90 _____ .

C
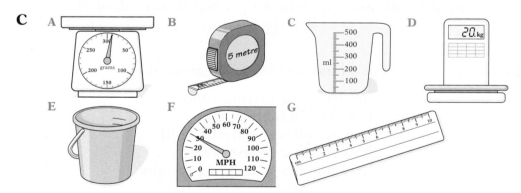

What could you use to measure these?
Choose from the pictures above.
Some will have more than 1 answer.
1. how much a book weighs
2. how long a room is
3. how much a bird weighs
4. how much milk a bowl holds
5. how long a fence is
6. how much water a tub holds
7. how far it is from one town to the next
8. how long a finger is

◄◄ CHAPTER REVIEW ◄◄

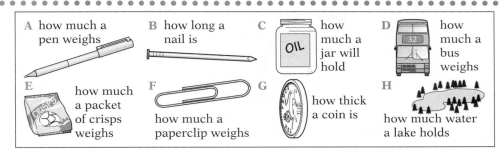

A how much a pen weighs

B how long a nail is

C how much a jar will hold — OIL

D how much a bus weighs — 32

E how much a packet of crisps weighs — CRISPS

F how much a paperclip weighs

G how thick a coin is

H how much water a lake holds

◄◄ Exercise 1 on page 250

A Write down the letters of the things in the box that we measure in millimetres.

◄◄ Exercise 2 on page 251

B Write down the letters of the things in the box that we measure in millilitres.

◄◄ Exercise 3 on page 251

C Write down the letters of the things in the box that we measure in grams.

◄◄ Exercise 4 on page 252

D What are these arrows pointing to?

1.
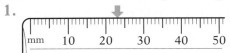

2.
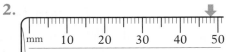

◄◄ Exercise 4 on page 252

E How long are these?

1.
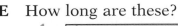
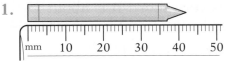

2.

◄◄ Exercise 5 on page 253

F How much do these weigh?

1.
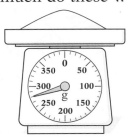

2.
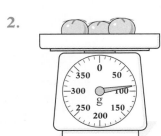

◀◀
Exercise 6
on page 254

G   How much do these weigh?

1.

2.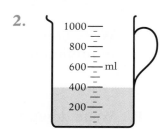

◀◀
Exercise 7
on page 255

H   How much water is in these?

1.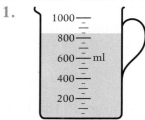

2.

km	m	cm	mm	mile	*l*	m*l*
	pint	kg	g	pound		

◀◀
Exercise 8
on page 258

I   What is it best to measure these in?
Choose from the box.

1. how high a barn is   2. how long a cat's tail is
3. how much a rabbit weighs   4. how much a big pot holds
5. how much a bike weighs   6. how long a nail is
7. how far it is to the next city   8. how much a rat weighs

◀◀
Exercise 9
on page 258

J   What goes in the gap?
Choose from the box above.

1. A pencil could be about 20 _____ long.
2. A heater could be about 1 _____ high.
3. Jason's hair is very short. It is about 15 _____ long.
4. A tin of baked beans could weigh about 400 _____ .

◀◀
Exercise 10
on page 259

K   What would you use to measure these?
Choose from the pictures.

1. how much a bike weighs   2. how much a pot holds
3. how long a nail is   4. how far it is between
two towns

20 Negative Numbers

The temperature in some places is below zero.
What does this mean?
Find out how far below zero temperatures can go.

Negative numbers

We measure temperatures in degrees.
Water freezes at 0 degrees.
We write this as 0 °C.
Sometimes the temperature goes **below 0 °C**.
−2 °C means 2 degrees below zero.

Exercise 1

What goes in the gap?

1. −5 °C means _5 °C_ below zero.

2. −7 °C means _____ below zero.

3. −10 °C means _____ below zero.

4. _____ means 25 °C below zero.

5. _____ means 60 °C below zero.

This is a thermometer.
It has a scale which goes below zero.

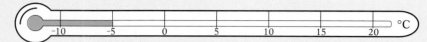

This thermometer reads −5 °C.

Exercise 2

What temperature do these read?

1.

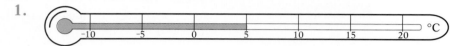

2.

3.

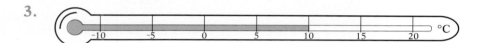

4.

Exercise 3

Which of these reads −7 °C?

A

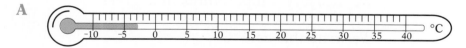

B

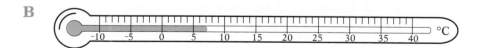

C

D

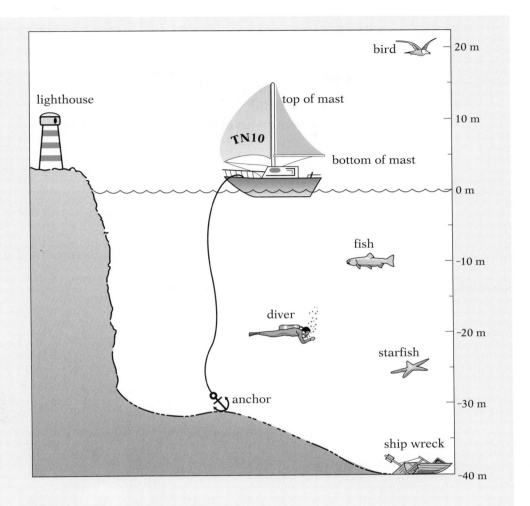

Example   The starfish is at about –25 m.
–25 m means 25 m below sea level.

Exercise 4   **A**   Look at the picture above.
1.   What is at about 20 m?
2.   What is at about –20 m?

B   What goes in the gap?
1.   The top of the mast is at about _____.
2.   The anchor is at about _____.
3.   The ship wreck is at about _____.
4.   The bottom of the mast is at about _____.
5.   The fish is at about _____.

The water level in this lake is
2 m below normal.
We say the water level is −2 m.

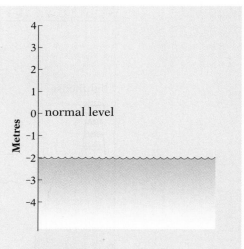

Exercise 5   Write down what the water level is.

1.
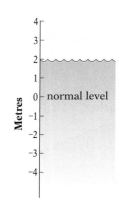

2.
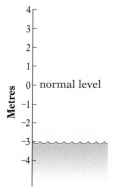

3.
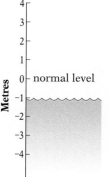

Numbers less than zero are called **negative numbers**.
This is a number line.
It shows **negative** and **positive** numbers.

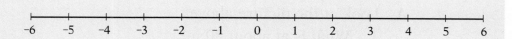

Example   The arrow at **A** is pointing to −2.

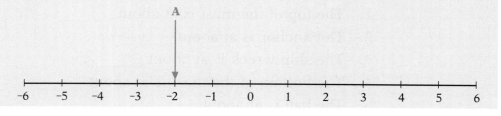

Exercise 6   Write down the numbers these arrows are pointing to.

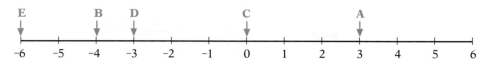

Sometimes not all the numbers are written on the scale.

Example

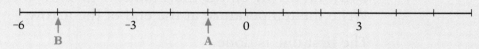

What number is the arrow at **A** pointing to?
What number is the arrow at **B** pointing to?

Answer

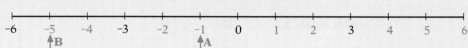

We fill in the missing numbers first.
The arrow at A is pointing to −1.
The arrow at B is pointing to −5.

Exercise 7   **A**

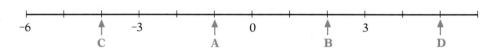

What numbers are these arrows pointing to?

1. **A**   2. **B**   3. **C**   4. **D**

B

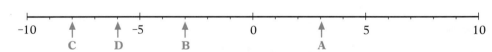

What numbers are these arrows pointing to?

1. **A**   2. **B**   3. **C**   4. **D**

Exercise 8   Use a copy of this number line.

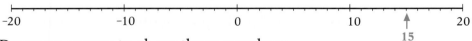

Draw an arrow to show these numbers.
Write the number beside the arrow.
The first one is done.

1. 15   2. −15   3. 5   4. −18

Exercise 9   Use a copy of the thermometer.

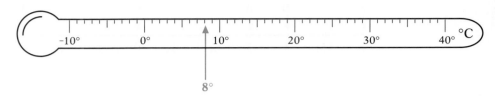

Draw an arrow on the thermometer to show these temperatures.
Write the temperature at the end of the arrow.

The first one is done.

1.	8 ° C	2.	35 °C	3.	2 °C	4.	−5 °C
5.	−3 °C	6.	5 °C	7.	−1 °C	8.	39 °C
9.	14 °C	10.	−8 °C				

Sam had to do 20 minutes homework.
He had done 12 minutes.

He pressed **1** **2** **−** **2** **0** **=** to get   *-8.*

He has 8 minutes left to do.

Investigation

Do these on your calculator.

8 − 10	10 − 8	16 − 20	12 − 16	20 − 8
8 − 20	15 − 7	7 − 15	40 − 16	16 − 40

Copy and fill in the gaps with *bigger* or *smaller*.

*When we subtract a _____ number from a _____ number on
the calculator we get a negative answer.*

Homework/Review 1

A   **What do dogs have that no other animals have?**

Use a copy of the box below.

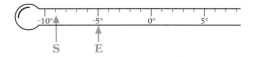

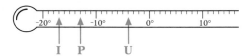

$$\overline{} \quad \overline{} \quad \overline{} \quad \overline{} \quad \overline{} \quad \overline{} \quad \overset{S}{\overline{}}$$
$$-13\,°C \quad -4\,°C \quad -13\,°C \quad -13\,°C \quad -17\,°C \quad -5\,°C \quad -9\,°C$$

B

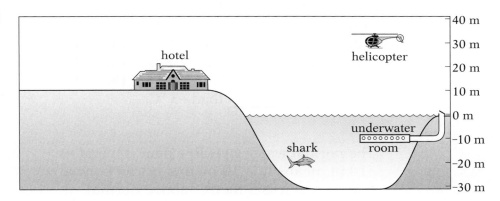

What goes in the gaps?

1. The helicopter is at about _____.
2. The underwater room is at about _____.
3. The top of the hotel is about _____.
4. The shark is at about _____.

C   Use a copy of the thermometer.

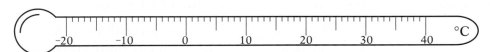

Draw an arrow to show these temperatures.
Write the temperature at the end of the arrow.

   1. 26 °C   2. −7 °C   3. 32 °C   4. −16 °C

Using negative numbers

−10 °C is **colder** than −2 °C.
−10 °C is further below zero than −2 °C.

−3 °C is **warmer** than −20 °C.
−3 °C is not as far below zero as −20 °C.

Exercise 10   What goes in the gap, **colder** or **warmer**?

1. −5 °C is _colder_ than 0 °C.   2. −7 °C is _____ than 10 °C.
3. 8 °C is _____ than −1 °C.   4. −1 °C is _____ than 0 °C.
5. −10 °C is _____ than 1 °C.   6. −20 °C is _____ than 10 °C.
7. 22 °C is _____ than −15 °C.   8. 5 °C is _____ than −3 °C.
9. −4 °C is _____ than −3 °C.   10. −12 °C is _____ than 1 °C.
11. −6 °C is _____ than −7 °C.   12. −18 °C is _____ than −5 °C.
13. −5 °C is _____ than −9 °C.   14. −14 °C is _____ than −20 °C.
15. 3 °C is _____ than −20 °C.   16. −1 °C is _____ than −3 °C.
17. 0 °C is _____ than −2 °C.   18. −16 °C is _____ than −48 °C.
19. −7 °C is _____ than −3 °C.

The normal water level in a dam is 0 metres.
−10 m means it is 10 metres below normal.
5 m means it is 5 metres above normal.

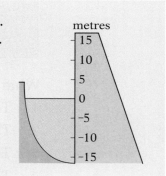

metres

Example   −2 m is a lower water level than −1 m.

Exercise 11   What goes in the gap, **lower** or **higher**?

1. −3 m is a _____ water level than 4 m.
2. 6 m is a _____ water level than 10 m.
3. 4 m is a _____ water level than −1 m.
4. −10 m is a _____ water level than −5 m.
5. −8 m is a _____ water level than −13 m.
6. −3 m is a _____ water level than −7 m.

Example

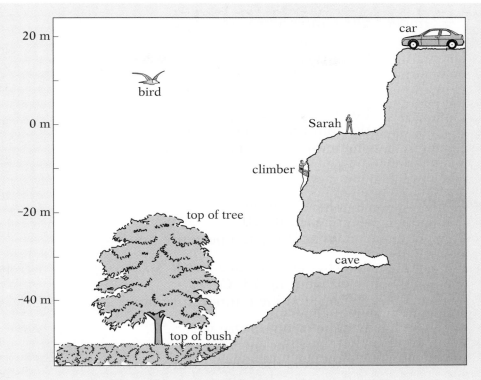

Sarah drew this picture to show what was above and below her.
What is about 30 m higher than the top of the bush?

Answer   Each mark is 10 m.
We must count up 3 marks from the top of the bush.
The top of the tree is 30 m above the top of the bush.

Exercise 12   Look at the picture above.

1. What is about 10 m higher than the top of the tree?
2. What is about 20 m higher than the climber?
3. What is about 40 m lower than the bird?
4. What is about 50 m higher than the cave?
5. What is about 20 m higher than the top of the bush?
6. What is about 30 m lower than Sarah?
7. What is about 10 m lower than the top of the tree?
8. What is about 60 m higher than the top of the bush?
9. What is about 30 m lower than the car?
10. What is about 20 m lower than the cave?

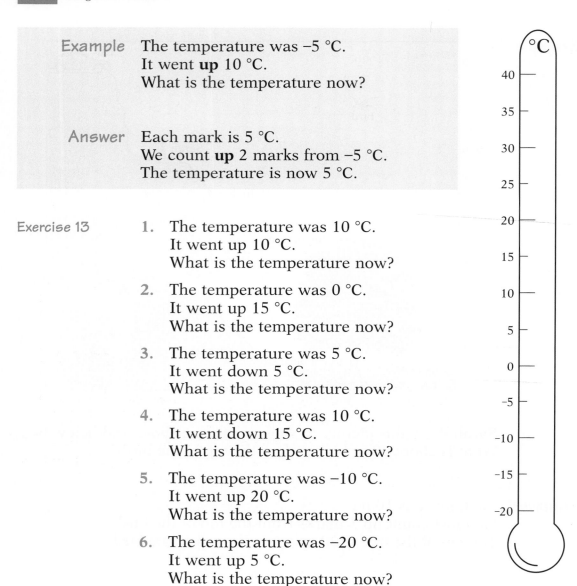

Example   The temperature was –5 °C.
It went **up** 10 °C.
What is the temperature now?

Answer   Each mark is 5 °C.
We count **up** 2 marks from –5 °C.
The temperature is now 5 °C.

Exercise 13

1.   The temperature was 10 °C.
It went up 10 °C.
What is the temperature now?

2.   The temperature was 0 °C.
It went up 15 °C.
What is the temperature now?

3.   The temperature was 5 °C.
It went down 5 °C.
What is the temperature now?

4.   The temperature was 10 °C.
It went down 15 °C.
What is the temperature now?

5.   The temperature was –10 °C.
It went up 20 °C.
What is the temperature now?

6.   The temperature was –20 °C.
It went up 5 °C.
What is the temperature now?

7.   The temperature was 15 °C.
It went down 20 °C.
What is the temperature now?

8.   The temperature was –20 °C.
It went up 10 °C.
What is the temperature now?

9.   The temperature was –5 °C.
It went down 15 °C.
What is the temperature now?

Homework/Review 2

A Which word, **colder** or **warmer**, goes in the gap?

1. 7 °C is _____ than 2 °C.   2. 10 °C is _____ than 0 °C.
3. −3 °C is _____ than 0 °C.   4. −5 °C is _____ than −2 °C.
5. −10 °C is _____ than 5 °C.   6. 4 °C is _____ than −1 °C.
7. −7 °C is _____ than −12 °C.

B Simon drew this picture to
show what was above and below him.

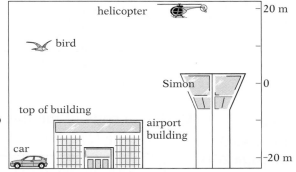

1. What is about 20 m
   higher than Simon?
2. What is about 10 m
   lower than Simon?
3. What is about 30 m
   higher than the top
   of the airport building?
4. What is about 30 m
   lower than the bird?
5. What is about 10 m lower than the top of the airport building?
6. What is about 40 m higher than the car?

C 1. The temperature was −10 °C.
   It went up 10 °C.
   What is the temperature now?

2. The temperature was −5 °C.
   It went up 15 °C.
   What is the temperature now?

3. The temperature was 15 °C.
   It went down 20 °C.
   What is the temperature now?

4. The temperature was −5 °C.
   It went down 5 °C.
   What is the temperature now?

5. The temperature was −10 °C.
   It went up 20 °C.
   What is the temperature now?

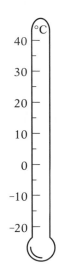

◀◀ CHAPTER REVIEW ◀◀

◀◀
Exercises 4
and 12
on pages 265
and 271

A What goes in the gap?
1. The fish is at about _____ .
2. The top of the funnel is at about _____ .
3. The gold coins are about 20 m lower than the _____ .
4. The _____ is about 30 m higher than the jellyfish.

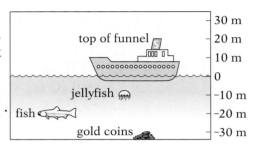

◀◀
Exercise 7
on page 267

B What numbers are these arrows pointing to?

1.

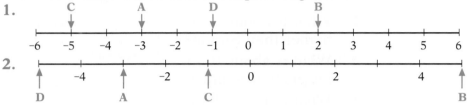

2.

◀◀
Exercise 9
on page 268

C Use a copy of the thermometer.

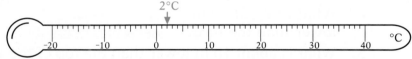

Draw an arrow on the thermometer to show these temperatures.
Write the temperature at the end of the arrow.
The first one is done.

1. 2 °C   2. 15 °C   3. −8 °C   4. −16 °C

◀◀
Exercise 10
on page 270

D What goes in the gap, **colder** or **warmer**?
1. −3 °C is _____ than 0 °C.   2. 4 °C is _____ than −10 °C.
3. −6 °C is _____ than −2 °C.   4. −5 °C is _____ than −16 °C.

◀◀
Exercise 13
on page 272

E 1. The temperature was −20 °C.
It went up 15 °C.
What is the temperature now?
2. The temperature was 5 °C.
It went down 20 °C.
What is the temperature now?

21 Pictograms

Keeping count..............................

Many years ago people kept count by drawing pictures on cave walls.

What might these pictures be for?

Reading pictograms

This table shows the number of cakes sold.

Day	Number
Monday	5
Tuesday	3
Wednesday	6
Thursday	4
Friday	2

Greg drew this **pictogram**.

A pictogram is a picture graph.

Has Greg drawn the right number of cakes?

Day	Number
Monday	⊙ ⊙ ⊙ ⊙ ⊙
Tuesday	⊙ ⊙ ⊙
Wednesday	⊙ ⊙ ⊙ ⊙ ⊙ ⊙
Thursday	⊙ ⊙ ⊙ ⊙
Friday	⊙ ⊙
Each ⊙ stands for 1 cake.	

Exercise 1

A Lisa asked her friends which bar they liked best.
She drew this pictogram.

1. How many liked Time Out best?
2. How many liked Flake best?
3. How many friends did Lisa ask?

Chocolate Bar	
Time out	🍫🍫🍫🍫🍫🍫
Aero	🍫🍫🍫🍫
Twix	🍫🍫🍫
Flake	🍫🍫🍫🍫🍫🍫🍫🍫🍫
🍫 stands for 1 person	

B Ron counted how many lights were on. Use a copy of this pictogram. There were 6 lights on in Room 3 and 3 lights on in Room 4. Show this on your pictogram.

Room	
Room 1	💡
Room 2	💡 💡 💡 💡 💡
Room 3	
Room 4	
💡 stands for 1 light	

Example 🐱 stands for 5 cats. How many cats does 🐱 🐱 🐱 stand for?

Answer 🐱 🐱 🐱 stands for 15 cats.

Ways to help you

- **Count**

  If 🥤 stands for 2 drinks, we count in twos.

  If 🐰 stands for 5 rabbits, we count in fives.

  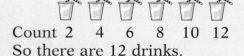

  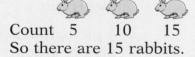

  Count 2 4 6 8 10 12
  So there are 12 drinks.

  Count 5   10   15
  So there are 15 rabbits.

- **Multiply**

  If ⚙ stands for 2 cars we multiply by 2.

  There are 7 ⚙, so we multiply 7 by 2.
  7 × 2 = 14   So there are 14 cars.

Exercise 2

A 👤 stands for 2 people.

How many do these stand for?

1. 👤👤 2. 👤👤👤👤👤 3. 👤👤👤👤

B 📕 stands for 10 books.

How many do these stand for?

1. 📕📕 2. 📕📕📕 3. 📕📕📕📕

C 🍔 stands for 5 burgers.

How many do these stand for?

1. 🍔🍔🍔 2. 🍔🍔🍔🍔🍔🍔🍔

3. 🍔🍔🍔🍔 4. 🍔🍔🍔🍔🍔🍔

Exercise 3

Use a copy of these tables.

Fill in the numbers on them.

1.

Cars outside gate 🚗 stands for 10 cars		
Before school	🚗 🚗 🚗 🚗	40
Lunch time	🚗 🚗 🚗	
After school	🚗 🚗	

2.

Drinks sold 🥤 stands for 2 drinks		
Coffee	🥤🥤🥤🥤🥤🥤🥤🥤	16
Tea	🥤🥤🥤🥤🥤	
Hot chocolate	🥤🥤🥤	
Coke	🥤🥤🥤🥤🥤🥤🥤🥤🥤🥤	
Orange	🥤🥤🥤🥤	
Milk	🥤🥤	

3.

Trees planted		Each picture stands for 100 trees
Fir	🌲🌲🌲🌲	400
Oak	🌳🌳	
Elm	🌳🌳🌳🌳🌳🌳	
Ash	🌳🌳🌳🌳🌳🌳	

4.

Number of chocolate bars sold		▯ stands for 5 bars
Monday	▯▯▯▯	20
Tuesday	▯▯▯	
Wednesday	▯▯▯▯▯	
Thursday	▯▯▯▯▯▯	
Friday	▯▯▯▯▯▯▯	

Example Sam counted the songs on the radio last Saturday. He drew this pictogram.
1. How many songs were played in the morning?
2. How many songs were played at night?

Time	Number
morning	🐑🐑🐑
afternoon	🐑🐑🐑🐑🐑
night	🐑🐑🐑🐑🐑🐑🐑

🐑 stands for 10 songs

Answer 1. 🐑🐑🐑 is 3 × 10 which is 30 songs.

2. 🐑🐑🐑🐑🐑🐑🐑 is 7 × 10 which is 70 songs.

Exercise 4 **A** Ros counted the number of top 20 songs played on the radio. She drew this pictogram.
1. How many top 20 songs were there in the afternoon?
2. How many top 20 songs were there at night?
3. How many top 20 songs did Ros count altogether?

Time	Number of top 20 songs
morning	♪♪♪
afternoon	♪♪♪♪♪
night	♪♪♪♪♪♪♪

♪ stands for 10 songs

B Ros drew this pictogram to show how often her friends listened to the radio.

stands for 2 people	
a lot	🎙️ 🎙️ 🎙️ 🎙️
sometimes	🎙️ 🎙️ 🎙️
never	🎙️

  1. How many people listened to the radio a lot?

  2. How many never listened to it?

  3. How many listened to it sometimes?

C Ros drew this pictogram to show what radio station people liked best.

Station	Number
Station 1	🧍 🧍
Station 2	🧍
Station 3	🧍 🧍 🧍
Station 4	🧍
stands for 5 people	

  1. How many liked station 1 best?

  2. How many liked station 3 best?

  3. How many liked station 4 best?

  4. How many people did Ros ask?

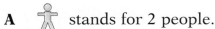 stands for 10 boxes.

To show 5 boxes we use half a picture.

stands for 5 boxes.

Exercise 5

A 🧍 stands for 2 people.

How many do these stand for?

  1.   2.   3.

B 💿 stands for 10 CDs.

How many do these stand for?

  1.   2.   3.

C 🗂️ stands for 20 cards.

How many do these stand for?

  1.   2.   3.

Example   stands for 10 trees.   stands for 5 trees.

stands for less than 5 trees.

stands for more than 5 trees.

Exercise 6   **1.** stands for 10 books.

Which of these could stand for 2 books?

A   B   C

2. stands for 10 sandwiches.

Which of these could stand for 8 sandwiches?

A   B   C

Exercise 7   **A**   This pictogram shows the number of rainy days.

How many rainy days were there in

1. February
2. March
3. April?

Month	stands for 2 rainy days
January	
February	
March	
April	

B   This pictogram shows the number of cloudy days.

1. How many cloudy days were there in April?
2. How many cloudy days were there in January?

Month	stands for 10 cloudy days
January	
February	
March	
April	

3. Ben said 'There were 25 cloudy days in February'.
   Explain why he was **wrong**.

4. Which of these is the number of cloudy days in March?
   20   25   30   27

C This pictogram shows the weather over 4 months.
   Each picture stands for 10 days.

1. Which of these is the
   number of sunny days?
      60   68   63

sunny	
cloudy	
rainy	

2. Ben said 'There were
   25 cloudy days'.
   Explain why he was **wrong**.

3. Do you think these months were in summer or winter?

Homework/Review 1

A   stands for £5.

How many pounds do these stand for?

1.   2.   3.

B Use a copy of this table. Finish filling it in.

Amount of pocket money	Each picture stands for 2 people	
none	🚶🚶🚶🚶🚶🚶	12
50p	🚶🚶🚶🚶	
£1	🚶🚶🚶🚶🚶🚶🚶	
more than £1	🚶🚶🚶	

C Are these sentences *true* or *not true*?

1. There were 40 packets
   of crisps sold.

2. There were 75 ice-creams sold.

3. There were 85 cold drinks sold.

4. There were 15 hot drinks sold.

Items sold	
crisps	🍟🍟🍟🍟
ice-creams	🍦🍦🍦🍦🍦🍦
hot drinks	☕🍵
cold drinks	🥤🥤🥤🥤🥤🥤🥤🥤
Each picture stands for 10	

D This pictogram shows the number of cows on some farms.

	stands for 10 cows
Farm 1	🐄🐄🐄🐄🐄🐄🐄
Farm 2	🐄🐄🐄🐄🐄
Farm 3	🐄🐄🐄🐄
Farm 4	🐄🐄🐄🐄🐄🐄🐄🐄

1. How many cows are there on Farm 1?

2. Ray thought there were 45 cows on Farm 3. Explain why he was **wrong**.

3. Which of these is the number of cows on Farm 4?
    70   75   80   78

Drawing pictograms

This table shows the number of pupils away from school. Sam drew a pictogram to show this.

He chose 🧍 to stand for 2 pupils.

Day	Number away
Monday	4
Tuesday	5
Wednesday	2
Thursday	6
Friday	7

For Monday,

4 pupils = 🧍🧍 2 + 2

For Tuesday,

5 pupils = 🧍🧍⃪ 2 + 2 + 1

Has Sam worked out the other days right?

Day	Number away
Monday	🧍🧍
Tuesday	🧍🧍⃪
Wednesday	🧍
Thursday	🧍🧍🧍
Friday	🧍🧍🧍⃪
🧍 stands for 2 pupils	

Exercise 8   Use a copy of these.
Finish the pictogram for each table.

1.

Where born	Number
England	40
Scotland	5
Wales	10
Ireland	10
Other	20

Where born	
England	🧍🧍🧍🧍🧍🧍🧍🧍
Scotland	
Wales	
Ireland	
Other	
🧍 stands for 5 people	

2.

Colour of car	Number
red	4
blue	7
green	8
yellow	3
white	10
grey	1

Colour of car	
red	
blue	
green	⊚ ⊚
yellow	
white	
grey	

⊚ stands for 2 cars

3.

Like doing	Number
disco	20
skating	45
cinema	15
ten pin	22

Like doing	
disco	✓ ✓
skating	
cinema	
ten pin	

✓ stands for 10 people

Exercise 9

A Jim asked his friends what they wore on Saturday.
He drew this pictogram.

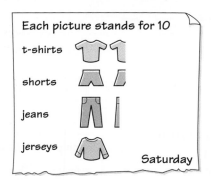

1. How many wore t-shirts?

2. How many wore shorts?

3. How many wore jerseys?

4. Which of these is the number who wore jeans?

    10   15   12   18   22

B. The pictogram below shows what Jim's friends wore on Sunday. Use a copy of this pictogram.

1. 40 people wore jeans.
   Show this on the pictogram.

2. 32 people wore a jersey.
   Show this on the pictogram.

C. Look at both of Jim's pictograms. Which day do you think was colder? How can you tell?

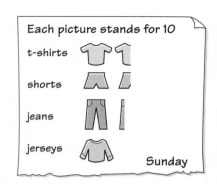

Homework/Review 2

A Use a copy of this. Finish the pictogram.

Day	Number
Mon	10
Tue	11
Wed	13
Fri	9

Day	
Mon	🔲 🔲 🔲 🔲 🔲
Tue	
Wed	
Fri	
🔲 stands for 2	

B Elen asked her friends what they did one weekend. She drew this pictogram.

1. How many went swimming?

2. How many played tennis?

3. Which of these is the number who went on go karts?

   10   15   20   12

C Elen asked her friends
again 6 months later.
She drew a pictogram.

Use a copy of this
pictogram.

Each picture stands for 10

swimming

tennis

skating

go karts

Weekend 2

1. 30 people went
skating.
Show this on
your pictogram.

2. 28 people went
on go karts.
Show this on
your pictogram.

D Look at both of Elen's pictograms.
Which one do you think was drawn in winter?
How can you tell?

Task

1. Ask your friends one of
these questions.
    How many brothers
    have you got?
    What month were you
    born in?
    Which of these animals
    do you like best?

    dog   cat   horse   rabbit

    Which of these sports
    do you play?

    football   netball   hockey   cricket

    How many hours did you watch TV
    last night?

2. Make up a collection sheet for the answers.

3. Draw a pictogram.

◀◀ CHAPTER REVIEW ◀◀

◀◀
Exercise 2
on page 277

A 🍬 stands for 5 sweeets.

How many do these stand for?

1. 🍬 🍬   2. 🍬 🍬 🍬 🍬 🍬

◀◀
Exercise 3
on page 277

B Use a copy of this table. Fill it in.

Month	CDs sold	⊙ Stands for 100 CDs
April	⊙ ⊙ ⊙ ⊙	400
May	⊙ ⊙ ⊙	
June	⊙ ⊙ ⊙ ⊙ ⊙ ⊙	
July	⊙ ⊙ ⊙ ⊙ ⊙ ⊙ ⊙ ⊙	

◀◀
Exercise 4
on page 278

C Ros asked her friends when they listened to the radio. She drew this pictogram.

1. How many listened to the radio in the morning?

2. How many listened at night?

3. How many friends did Ros ask?

When	Number
morning	🧍 🧍 🧍 🧍 🧍 🧍
after school	🧍 🧍 🧍
night	🧍 🧍 🧍 🧍 🧍
🧍 stands for 2 people	

◀◀
Exercise 7
on page 280

D This pictogram shows how hot it was.

1. How many days was it very hot?

2. How many days was it cool?

3. Which of these is the number of warm days?

50   60   55   58

4. Which of these is the number of cold days?

10   15   18   13

5. Do you think these months were in summer or winter?

Each whole picture stands for 10 days	
very hot	🌡
hot	🌡 🌡 🌡 ◖
warm	🌡 🌡 🌡 🌡 🌡 🌡
cool	🌡 🌡
cold	🌡 ◖

E Use a copy of this.
Finish the pictogram.

◄◄
Exercise 8
on page 282

Colour of Rabbit	Number
Black	2
White	4
Grey	6
Brown	5
Other	11

Colour of Rabbit	
Black	🐰
White	
Grey	
Brown	
Other	
🐰 stands for 4 rabbits	

F Jim asked his friends what they did one Saturday.
He drew this pictogram.

◄◄
Exercise 7
on page 280

1. How many went to the cinema?
2. How many went swimming?
3. Which of these is the number who went to the fun park?

42   40   45   48

Each whole picture stands for 10	
watched a video	
went to the cinema	
went swimming	
went to the fun park	

1st Saturday

G Jim asked his friends what they did another Saturday.
Use a copy of the pictogram.

◄◄
Exercise 9
on page 283

1. 35 people went to the cinema. Show this on your pictogram.
2. 2 people went swimming. Show this on your pictogram.

Each whole picture stands for 10	
watched a video	
went to the cinema	
went swimming	
went to the fun park	

1st Saturday

H Look at both of Jim's pictograms.
What can you tell about the weather on these days?

◄◄
Exercise 9
on page 283

Quick Test 7

A   Colin was a cook at the South Pole.

How much of each of these did he use?

1. 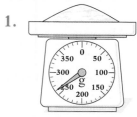   2. 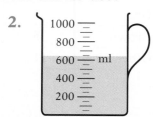   3.

B

What is it best to measure these in?
Choose from the box.

1.   how wide a teaspoon is

2.   how much a small fish weighs

3.   how much a cup will hold

C

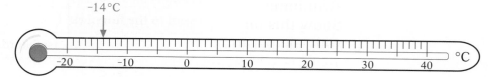

What goes in the gaps? Choose from the box.

1.   A knife could be about _____ mm long.

2.   An eggcup could hold about _____ ml.

3.   A book could weigh about _____ grams.

D   Use a copy of the thermometer.

−14 °C

```
          -20      -10       0       10       20       30       40      °C
```

Draw an arrow to show these.
Write the temperature next to the arrow.
The first one is done.

1.   −14 °C   2.   7 °C   3.   −7 °C   4.   −3 °C

E

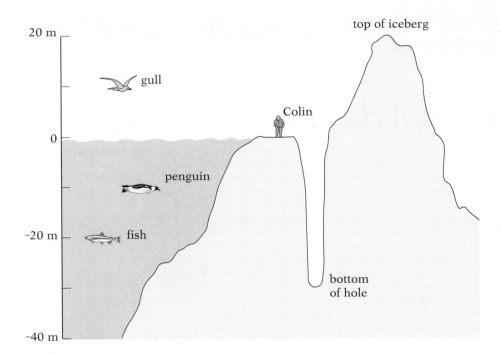

What goes in the gap?
The first one is done.

1. The fish is at about _−20 m_ .

2. The penguin is at about _____ .

3. The bottom of the hole is about _____ lower than Colin.

4. The gull is about 30 m higher than _____ .

5. The bottom of the hole is about 40 m lower than _____ .

F Colin asked the people at the South Pole which animal they liked.
Use a copy of this pictogram.

1. How many people liked penguins?

2. Colin thought that 25 liked sea lions. Explain why Colin was **wrong**.

3. 45 liked seals. Show this on your pictogram.

Use ⌒ for the picture.

Each whole picture stands for 10		
penguins		
sea lions		
seals		

22 More Adding and Subtracting

On holiday ....

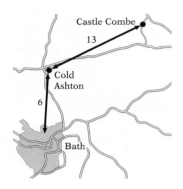

People on holiday often have to add and subtract.
What might you have to add and subtract at these places?

- a cafe
- a hotel
- a bus trip
- the motorway
- the ferry
- the beach

Adding to 99

Remember . . .

The addition facts you learnt in **Chapter 3**.

46	We add the ones first.
+ 3	6 ones + 3 ones is 9 ones.
49	Then add the tens.
	4 tens + 0 tens is 4 tens.

52	2 ones + 2 ones is 4 ones.
+ 12	5 tens +1 ten is 6 tens
64	

Exercise 1   Copy these and fill in the answers.

1.   23
    + 4

2.   52
    + 5

3.   61
    + 8

4.   43
    + 6

5. 21   6. 33   7. 81   8. 34
   + 13   + 14   + 16   + 20

9. 46   10. 52   11. 63
   + 32   + 26   + 35

Sometimes additions are written as 24 + 36.
We write them as   24   before we do them.
                   + 36

Exercise 2   Find the answer to these.

1. 23 + 36   2. 51 + 27   3. 82 + 14

4. 43 + 25   5. 60 + 19   6. 46 + 23

7. 58 + 31   8. 65 + 23

We can show 37 + 5 like this.

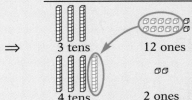

7 ones + 5 ones is 12 ones.

12 ones is 1 ten and 2 ones.
We add the 1 ten to the tens.

So we get 4 tens and 2 ones.

The answer is 42.

Example   36   6 ones + 9 ones is 15 ones.
                +.9   15 ones is 1 ten and 5 ones.
                45 ——Write down the 5 ones.
                      Add the 1 ten to the tens.

Exercise 3   Copy these and fill in the answers.

1. 27   2. 39   3. 52   4. 46
   + 6   + 7   + 9   + 7

5.	36 + 8	**6.**	78 + 7	**7.**	64 + 7	**8.**	87 + 5
9.	75 + 9	**10.**	39 + 8	**11.**	36 + 9		

Exercise 4   Find the answers to these.

1. 53 + 8   2. 64 + 9   3. 45 + 7
4. 39 + 6   5. 69 + 3   6. 55 + 9
7. 67 + 9   8. 49 + 9   9. 58 + 8
10. 47 + 9   11. 38 + 7

Example 64 + 28

Answer   64   4 + 8 = 12 which is 1 ten and 2 ones.
+ 28   Write the 2 down.
92   Add the 1 ten to the tens.
6 + 2 + 1 = 9

Exercise 5   Copy these and fill in the answers.

1. 28   2. 37   3. 29   4. 64
  + 36   + 46   + 43   + 17

5. 58   6. 49   7. 37   8. 35
  + 39   + 25   + 48   + 58

Exercise 6   Use a copy of these.
Fill in the missing numbers.

1.
+	27	19	32
46			
57			
39			

2.
+	19	28	16
57			
64			
71			

3.
+	29	38	49
26			
35			
42			

We can add more than 2 numbers.

17   7 + 5 + 9 = 21 which is 2 tens and 1 one.
25   Write down the 1.
+ 39   Add the 2 tens to the tens.
81   1 + 2 + 3 + 2 = 8

Exercise 7   Copy these and fill in the answers.

1.   18   2.   19   3.   8   4.   23
     34   35   37   29
   + 27   + 37   + 45   + 28

5.   17   6.   63   7.   54
     23   15   21
   + 19   + 11   + 9

Remember . . . Magic squares

We get the same number no matter which way we add.

Exercise 8   Which one of these is **not** a magic square?

A

42	14	34
22	30	38
26	46	18

B

40	10	30
18	26	34
22	32	14

Example   Bill spent £27 last week and £35 this week.
          How much has he spent in the two weeks?

Answer   27
           +₁35   Bill has spent £62.
             62

Exercise 9   **A** 1. Helen had 27 books in her bookcase.
                        She had 11 books under her bed.
                        How many did she have altogether?

                 2. Tony had 35 books in his bookcase.
                        He had 17 books under his bed.
                        How many did he have altogether?

                 3. Nesta had 47 books in her bookcase.
                        She had 17 books under her bed.
                        How many did she have altogether?

B Rita plays a game at a fair.
She throws 2 darts.
She wins if the numbers add to more than 80.
Which games did she win?

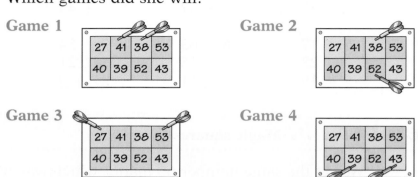

Game 1   Game 2

Game 3   Game 4

C Rishi plays another game at the fair.
He throws 2 balls.
He wins if the numbers that fall down add to 50 or 90.
What did Rishi get in these games?
Which did he win?

Game 1   Game 2

Game for 2 players: MAKE IT SMALL

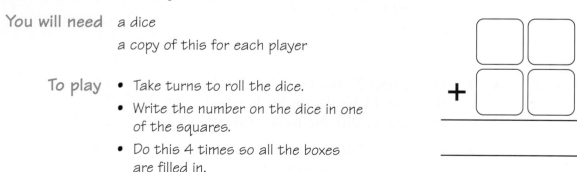

You will need   a dice
a copy of this for each player

To play   • Take turns to roll the dice.
          • Write the number on the dice in one
            of the squares.
          • Do this 4 times so all the boxes
            are filled in.
          • Do the addition.
          • The player with the smallest answer gets a point.
          • The player with the most points after 10 games wins.

Homework/Review 1

A Copy these and fill in the answers.

1. 　26
　　+ 2

2. 　34
　　+ 3

3. 　73
　　+ 26

4. 　81
　　+ 18

B Find the answers to these.

1. 43 + 8
2. 57 + 6
3. 35 + 7
4. 52 + 9
5. 69 + 8

C How can you dive without getting wet?

Use a copy of the box.

I　47 + 12 = 59
G　27 + 54
N　53 + 29
V　48 + 35
Y　69 + 28
O　45 + 25
D　38 + 54
K　75 + 18
S　62 + 29

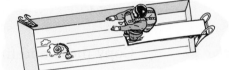

$\overline{81}$	$\overline{70}$		$\overline{91}$	$\overline{93}$	$\overline{97}$
	I		I		
$\overline{92}$	$\overline{59}$	$\overline{83}$	$\overline{59}$	$\overline{82}$	$\overline{81}$

D 1. There were 29 people on a bus.
Another 14 people got on.
How many were on the bus then?

2. Sam and Ben played a game on the computer.
The game had 2 parts.

Sam

Ben

How much did Sam get altogether?
How much did Ben get altogether?

Subtracting to 99

Remember . . .

The subtraction facts you learnt in **Chapter 4.**

$$
\begin{array}{r}
68 \\
-\ 5 \\
\hline
63
\end{array}
$$

Subtract the ones first
8 ones take away 5 ones is 3 ones

Then subtract the tens
6 tens take away 0 tens is 6 tens

$$
\begin{array}{r}
67 \\
-\ 13 \\
\hline
54
\end{array}
$$

7 ones take away 3 ones is 4 ones
6 tens take away 1 ten is 5 tens

Exercise 10   Copy these and fill in the answer.

1. $\begin{array}{r} 88 \\ -\ 6 \\ \hline \end{array}$ 2. $\begin{array}{r} 59 \\ -\ 7 \\ \hline \end{array}$ 3. $\begin{array}{r} 47 \\ -\ 5 \\ \hline \end{array}$ 4. $\begin{array}{r} 88 \\ -\ 13 \\ \hline \end{array}$

5. $\begin{array}{r} 79 \\ -\ 24 \\ \hline \end{array}$ 6. $\begin{array}{r} 88 \\ -\ 53 \\ \hline \end{array}$ 7. $\begin{array}{r} 69 \\ -\ 40 \\ \hline \end{array}$ 8. $\begin{array}{r} 66 \\ -\ 16 \\ \hline \end{array}$

9. $\begin{array}{r} 73 \\ -\ 33 \\ \hline \end{array}$ 10. $\begin{array}{r} 79 \\ -\ 50 \\ \hline \end{array}$ 11. $\begin{array}{r} 64 \\ -\ 32 \\ \hline \end{array}$ 12. $\begin{array}{r} 58 \\ -\ 24 \\ \hline \end{array}$

Sometimes, when we try to subtract, we can't.

$$
\begin{array}{r}
34 \\
-\ 8
\end{array}
$$

We can't take 8 away from 4.

We have to make one of the tens into 10 ones.

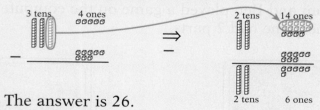

14 ones take away
8 ones is 6 ones.

2 tens   6 ones

The answer is 26.

Example   Find the answer to 53 − 17

$$
\begin{array}{r}
53 \\
-\ 17 \\
\hline
\end{array}
$$

We can't take
7 from 3.

$$
\begin{array}{r}
{}^4\!\cancel{5}3 \\
-\ 17 \\
\hline
\end{array}
$$

Make a ten
into 10 ones.

$$
\begin{array}{r}
{}^4\!\cancel{5}3 \\
-\ 17 \\
\hline
6
\end{array}
$$

13 − 7 = 6

$$
\begin{array}{r}
{}^4\!\cancel{5}3 \\
-\ 17 \\
\hline
36
\end{array}
$$

4 − 1 = 3

The answer is 36.

Exercise 11   Copy these and fill in the answers.

1.   54   2.   23   3.   64   4.   72
   − 15   − 17   − 26   − 35

5.   81   6.   44   7.   35   8.   96
   − 39   − 37   − 18   − 58

9.   77   10.   63   11.   84
   − 48   − 38   − 49

Exercise 12   Find the answers to these.

1. 73 − 27   2. 51 − 29   3. 34 − 19

4. 52 − 36   5. 43 − 27   6. 85 − 39

7. 92 − 56   8. 58 − 39   9. 65 − 37

10. 77 − 49   11. 84 − 56

Example   There were 42 eggs in a hen house.
             A fox ate 15 of them.
             How many were left?

Answer $^3\!4\!2$ Make a ten into 10 ones.
         − 15   12 ones take away 5 ones is 7 ones
           27   3 tens take away 1 ten is 2 tens

Exercise 13   A   1.   There were 29 eggs in a hen house.
                         A fox ate 13 of them.
                         How many were left?

               2.   There were 35 eggs in a hen house.
                    A fox ate 19 of them.
                    How many were left?

               3.   There were 43 eggs in a hen house.
                    A fox ate 25 of them.
                    How many were left?

B Ben bought these in the sale.
How much did he pay for each?

1.

2.

3.

Exercise 14

☐ – ☐ = 50

Find 5 ways to fill in the boxes to make 50.

Exercise 15

Make a copy of this magic square.
Fill in the missing numbers.

25		19
	16	
		7

Homework/Review 2

A Copy these and fill in the answer.

1.   87
    – 5

2.   58
    – 5

3.   39
    – 14

4.   75
    – 25

B What has 6 legs and
walks with only 4?

Use a copy of this box.

E   56 – 27 = 29
N   72 – 45
O   75 – 36
I   61 – 17
A   83 – 29
D   43 – 19
S   60 – 26
H   91 – 55
R   74 – 28

```
                                      E
___     ___  ___  ___  ___  ___
 54      36   39   46   34   29


                                      E
___  ___  ___       ___  ___  ___  ___  ___
 54   27   24        46   44   24   29   46
```

C   Use a copy of this magic square.
Fill in the missing numbers.

37	24	35
		34

D   1.   There were 46 apples in a box.
17 of them were eaten.
How many were left?

2.   Kate is 42.
Her son is 27 years younger.
How old is her son?

E   ☐ − ☐ = 20
Find 3 ways to fill in the boxes to make 20.

Investigation

This is a magic square.
Subtract 5 from every number.
Use an empty square and write
your answers on it.
Is your new square a magic square?

28	21	26
23	25	27
24	29	22

What happens if you subtract 4?
What happens if you subtract 6?
What happens if you subtract 7?
Is your new square always a magic square?

What happens if you add 4, 5, 6 or 7?

Copy this sentence and fill in the gap with *always* or *do not always*.

If you add or subtract the same number from every number in a magic square you _____ get a magic square.

◄◄ CHAPTER REVIEW ◄◄

◄◄
Exercise 1
on page 290

A   Copy these and fill in the answers.

1.   31
    + 6

2.   23
    + 6

3.   34
    + 14

4.   22
    + 35

◄◄
Exercise 3
on page 291

B   Copy these and fill in the answers.

1.   36
    + 9

2.   57
    + 6

3.   48
    + 5

4.   39
    + 7

Exercise 5
on page 292

C Copy these and fill in the answers.

1. 28
  + 36

2. 53
  + 29

3. 17
  + 59

4. 36
  + 57

Exercise 7
on page 293

D Copy these and fill in the answers.

1. 17
   21
 + 36

2. 33
   48
 + 15

3. 29
   34
 + 23

4. 19
   36
 + 37

Exercise 9
on page 293

E Sally plays a game at a fair.
She throws balls at a board.
If a number is hit, a green light comes on.
She wins if she scores over 90.
Which games did she win?

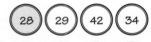

Game 1   **Game 2**   **Game 3**

Exercise 10
on page 296

F Copy these and fill in the answers.

1. 78
  − 5

2. 59
  − 13

3. 85
  − 24

4. 99
  − 57

Exercise 12
on page 297

G Find the answers to these.

1. 85 − 9
2. 73 − 28
3. 51 − 26
4. 63 − 38
5. 48 − 19
6. 92 − 57

Exercise 13
on page 297

H 1. There were 56 balls in a box.
A class took 37 of them.
How many were left?

2. What is the sale price
of this fishing set?

23 Tables. Lists. Charts

A day out ....

WILDLIFE PARK Times	
Mon	CLOSED
Tue - Thurs	12pm - 4pm
Fri	10am - 4pm
Sat/Sun	9am - 5pm
Closed	Xmas Day New Year's Day

WILDLIFE PARK Prices	
Adults	£12
Children (4-15)	£10
Under 4	Free
Family	£35

WILDLIFE PARK Tours	
Leave on the hour and take 50 minutes	
Adults	£5
Children (4-15)	£3
Under 4	Free
Family	£12

Peter and Maria went to the Wildlife Park.
They used these lists and charts to plan their day.

Think of somewhere you would like to go for a day.
What charts and lists might you use?

Reading tables, lists and charts

Example

Times to run 200 m

	Race 1	Race 2	Race 3	Race 4
Farid	28 seconds	27 seconds	28 seconds	27 seconds
Jason	26 seconds	26 seconds	26 seconds	27 seconds
David	29 seconds	27 seconds	28 seconds	29 seconds
Ed	29 seconds	30 seconds	30 seconds	31 seconds
Ravi	26 seconds	27 seconds	27 seconds	26 seconds

1. How long did David take to run Race 2?
2. Who ran fastest in Race 3?
3. Which boys ran faster than 28 seconds in Race 4?

Answers   1. 27 seconds   2. Jason   3. Farid and Jason and Ravi

Exercise 1

A

People at a fun park

	Wednesday	Thursday	Friday	Saturday	Sunday
number of adults	327	521	260	570	530
number of children	182	892	109	640	702

1. How many adults went to the park on Saturday?
2. How many people altogether went to the park on Friday?
3. One of the days was a school holiday.
   Which day do you think it was?
   Explain.

B

Spending at tuck shop

	January	February	March	April	May	June
7A	£52	£107	£123	£96	£119	£99
7B	£48	£96	£104	£89	£109	£98
7C	£57	£109	£115	£98	£124	£101
7D	£41	£83	£101	£84	£92	£92

1. Which class spent the most in March?
2. Which month did 7D spend the most?
3. How much did the four classes spend altogether in April?
4. The tuck shop was closed for 2 weeks in one month.
   Which month do you think it was?
   How can you tell this from the table?

C

Rider	Horse	Mark	Place
Jane	Sara	21	4th
Sam	Button	19	3rd
Nina	Teddy	16	1st
Jo	Batman	24	6th
Tandy	Ned	23	5th
Tom	Rex	17	2nd

1. Write down the name of Tandy's horse.
2. Which rider got 3rd?
3. Did you have to get the highest or lowest mark to win?

Example

HAIR CUTS

Cut - Women	£9.50	Blow Wave	£8.75
Men	£7.85	Colour and Cut	£21.50
Children	£6.75	Perm	£47.50

Mrs. Chan has a colour and cut.
Her 2 children have their hair cut.
How much will this cost altogether?

Answer   We must add £21.50 + £6.75 + £6.75.
Using a calculator we get £35.

Exercise 2   **A**

CHAN'S CAFE

Chicken and chips	£3.50
Bacon, egg and chips	£2.80
Burger and chips	£1.80
Pizza and chips	£2.50
Fish and chips	£1.95

1. How much does a burger and chips cost?
2. Which meal costs the most?
3. Gareth had pizza and chips.
   Dave had fish and chips.
   How much did this cost altogether?

B

apple	10 p	chocolate bar	30 p
banana	15 p	sandwich	50 p
crisps	15 p		

1. Gareth bought 2 apples and a bag of crisps.
   How much did these cost?
2. Dave had 50 p to spend.
   He spent it all.
   What could he have bought?

C How much does it cost to send these letters?

1. a 60 g letter second class
2. a 250 g letter first class
3. a 450 g letter second class
4. a 125 g letter first class
5. a 375 g letter second class
6. a 480 g letter first class

Cost to send a letter

Weight up to	First class	Second class
60 g	26 p	20 p
100 g	39 p	31 p
150 g	49 p	38 p
200 g	60 p	45 p
250 g	70 p	55 p
300 g	80 p	64 p
350 g	92 p	73 p
400 g	£1.04	83 p
450 g	£1.17	93 p
500 g	£1.30	£1.05

D

Prince Hotel

	NOV – APRIL	MAY – OCT
Single room	£45 a night	£60 a night
Double room	£60 a night	£85 a night
Family room	£70 a night	£95 a night
Dinner	£16	

1. Jo stayed a night in a single room in July. How much did this cost?

2. Mr. and Mrs. Smith stayed a night in a double room in March. How much did this cost?

3. The Lang Family stayed for 3 nights in a family room in August. How much did this cost?

4. Ben stayed for 4 nights in a single room in July. How much did this cost?

5. Ben had dinner on 3 nights and breakfast on 4 mornings. How much did this cost?

Distance charts

Example   **Distances in miles**

	Bristol	Glasgow	Hull	London
Bristol				
Glasgow	384			
Hull	230	254		
London	121	416	183	

To find the distance between Hull and Glasgow
     go **across** from Hull
     go **up** from Glasgow
     the box where the two lines meet gives the distance.
The distance is 254 miles.

To find the distance from Bristol to London
     go **up** from Bristol
     go **across** from London
     the box where the two lines meet gives the distance.
The distance is 121 miles.

Note We couldn't find the distance by
     going across from Bristol
     up from London
Why not?

Exercise 3 **A** Use the chart above for these.
1. How far is Glasgow from London?
2. How far apart are Hull and London?
3. Which two places are the longest distance apart?
4. Mr Banks drove from Glasgow to Bristol. How far did he drive?
5. Mr Banks then drove from Bristol to Hull. How far is this?
6. How far did Mr Banks drive altogether?

B   **Distances in miles**

	Belfast	Dublin	Larne	Sligo
Belfast				
Dublin	103			
Larne	23	127		
Sligo	126	133	149	

1. How far apart are Sligo and Dublin?
2. How far apart are Larne and Belfast?
3. Which place is 126 miles from Belfast?
4. Which two places are 103 miles apart?
5. Which place is the greatest distance from Larne?
6. Which place is the smallest distance from Dublin?
7. Mrs. Sims drove from Sligo to Belfast.
   Then she drove from Belfast to Dublin.
   How far did she drive altogether?

C   **Distances in miles**

	Brighton	Harwich	Manchester	Penzance
Brighton				
Harwich	125			
Manchester	260	264		
Penzance	300	404	363	

1. How far is it from Manchester to Harwich?
2. Which two places are 404 miles apart?
3. Which place is the shortest distance from Penzance?
4. Which two places are the shortest distance apart?
5. Pam drove from Harwich to Brighton.
   Then she drove from Brighton to Manchester.
   How far did she drive altogether?

Distances in miles

Cardiff					
233	Dover				
229	272	Leeds			
107	146	167	Oxford		
40	269	255	143	Swansea	
705	797	525	669	701	Thurso

To find the distance from Cardiff to Oxford
  go down from Cardiff
  go across from Oxford
  the box where the two lines meet gives the distance.
The distance is 107 miles.

Exercise 4   **A**   Use the chart above for these.
  1.   How far apart are Dover and Leeds?
  2.   How far apart are Swansea and Oxford?
  3.   Which two places are the shortest distance apart?
  4.   Which two places are 525 miles apart?
  5.   Which town is the shortest distance from Oxford?
  6.   Mrs. Map drove from Cardiff to Leeds.
      How far is this?
  7.   She then drove from Leeds to Oxford.
      How far is this?
  8.   How far did Mrs. Map drive altogether?

  B   Use the chart above for this.
      Rex had to write down the miles he drove for work.

Monday 4th May	Leeds to Swansea	255 miles
Tuesday 5th May	Swansea to Dover	

Use a copy of this table.
On Wednesday 6th May he drove from Dover to Cardiff.
Finish Rex's table.

We sometimes have to read charts to fill in order forms.

Exercise 5

item alarm clock
price £9.99
order number 220-742

item watch
price £14.99
order number 255-005

item Walkman
price £29.99
order number 575-222

item vase
price £4.99
order number 105-623

item camera
price £14.99
order number 440-881

Gary wanted to order these.
- 2 cameras
- 1 Walkman
- 1 watch
- 3 vases
- 2 alarm clocks

Use a copy of this form.
Fill it in.

ORDER BY POST				
Item	Order Number	Number wanted	Price each	Price
Camera	440-881	2	£14.99	£29.98
			Total amount	

Homework/Review 1

A

Number in library at lunchtime

	Monday	Tuesday	Wednesday	Thursday	Friday
Year 7	53	50	8	57	55
Year 8	64	61	59	108	60
Year 9	72	63	68	71	70

1. How many Year 8 pupils were in the library on Tuesday?
2. How many Year 9 pupils were in the library on Friday?
3. How many Year 7 pupils were in the library on Monday?
4. One day most of the Year 7 pupils were on a school trip.
   Which day do you think this was?
   How can you tell?

B

Ferry Prices			
NO CAR	Adult	Child (4-16)	Family
Day Return	£13	£7	£35
Overnight	£18	£10	£45
CAR (UP TO 5 PEOPLE)	Fri/Sat	Other days	
Day Return	£85	£75	
Overnight	£125	£105	

1. How much does it cost for a day return for an adult?
2. Mr. and Mrs. Watt bought 2 overnight tickets.
   They did not have a car.
   How much did these cost?
3. The Adams family of 4 went overnight by car on a Wedesday.
   How much did this cost?
4. Bob bought a ticket.
   It cost £125.
   What was his ticket for?

C   **Distances in miles**

	Aberdeen	Dundee	Liverpool	Plymouth
Aberdeen				
Dundee	67			
Liverpool	368	301		
Plymouth	641	574	302	

1. How far is it from Plymouth to Aberdeen?
2. Which two places are 574 miles apart?
3. Which place is the shortest distance from Dundee?
4. Which place is the longest distance from Liverpool?
5. Debbie drove from Dundee to Liverpool.
   How far is this?
6. Debbie then drove from Liverpool to Plymouth.
   How far is it from Liverpool to Plymouth?
7. How far did Debbie drive altogether?

Databases

Facts about people, animals, jobs or anything else can be kept on a **database**

Example

Name	Age	Class	School bus
Tom	11	7A	Yes
Colin	10	7B	No
Sue	11	7A	No
Wyn	12	7B	Yes
John	11	7B	Yes
Helen	11	7A	Yes

The pupils who are 11 are Tom, Sue, John and Helen.
The pupils in 7A who bus to school are Tom and Helen.
Which pupil in 7B is 11?

Exercise 6

A Write down the names of these.
   1. the children who have dogs
   2. the dogs older than 2
   3. the child who owns the pet named Rose
   4. the pets less than 5 years old

Child's name	Pet	Pet's name	Pet's age
Julie	cat	Ben	7
Mindu	dog	Bob	2
Ali	cat	Simba	3
Steve	rabbit	Fluff	5
Gwen	turtle	Rose	6
Dele	dog	Jake	5
Enid	dog	Jesse	4

B Write down the names of these.
   1. the people who went to France
   2. the people who had a holiday in July
   3. the people who went to Spain in September
   4. the person under 20 who went to France

Last holiday

Name	Age	Holiday place	Month
Mrs Green	53	Spain	Sept
Cath	21	France	Oct
Maya	17	Devon	July
Alex	14	France	July
Paul	25	Devon	Sept
Mr Taylor	63	Spain	Sept

C
1. What is Sam best at?
2. Write down the names of the boys.
3. Write down the names of those best at the beam.
4. How many girls in 7S are best at the floor?

The gym club

Name	Boy/girl	Class	Best at
Joy	girl	7T	beam
Pam	girl	7S	floor
Sam	boy	7T	bars
Sudi	girl	7T	box
Owen	boy	7S	beam
Lela	girl	7T	box
Val	girl	7S	floor

Homework/Review 2

1. What colour is Sandy?
2. How old is Buns?
3. What is the name of the 4-year-old dog?
4. Write down the names of the black animals.

Name	Animal	Age	Colour	Number
Coco	cat	2	black	827
Sandy	dog	5	tan	531
Tess	dog	4	black/white	625
Buns	rabbit	1	black	946
Candy	cat	3	tabby	714
Mugs	dog	1	tan	952

5. Write down the names of the dogs.
6. Write down the numbers of the cats.
7. How many tan dogs are there?
8. How many cats older than 2 are there?

 CHAPTER REVIEW

Exercise 1
on page 302

A   **Number of hours swimming**

	Week 1	Week 2	Week 3	Week 4	Week 5
Anna	4	3	5	5	6
Emma	7	5	6	5	3
Lyn	5	4	1	5	6
Mary	8	7	7	5	7

1. How long did Lyn swim for in week 3?
2. How long did Anna swim for in week 4?
3. Lyn was sick one week.
   Which week do you think this was?
   How can you tell?
4. How many hours did Mary swim altogether in weeks 4 and 5?

◀◀
Exercise 2
on page 303

B

PIZZA TO GO

	Small	Medium	Large
HAM	£3.50	£5	£6
MUSHROOM	£4.00	£6	£7
SPECIAL	£5.00	£7	£8.50
NO MEAT	£3.50	£5	£6
CHICKEN	£4.50	£6.50	£7.50

1. How much does a medium ham pizza cost?

2. How much does a small no meat pizza cost?

3. Three friends went out to dinner.
    They bought a large special and a small chicken pizza.
    How much did this cost?

◀◀
Exercise 3
on page 305

C   **Distances in miles**

	Cork	Galway	Limerick	Waterford
Cork				
Galway	122			
Limerick	58	64		
Waterford	73	141	77	

1. How far apart are Cork and Waterford?

2. Which place is 122 miles from Cork?

3. Which two places are 141 miles apart?

4. Which place is the shortest distance from Limerick?

5. Mr Pat drove from Limerick to Galway.
    He then drove from Galway to Cork.
    How far did he drive altogether?

◄◄ Exercise 5 on page 308

D

item discman
price £89.99
order number 575-250

item batteries
price £2.95 pack
order number 550-788

item lamp
price £29.99
order number 520-072

Joy wanted to order   1 discman
3 packs of batteries
2 lamps.
Use a copy of this order form.
Fill it in.

ORDER BY POST				
Item	Order number	Number wanted	Price each	Price
discman	575-250	1	£89.99	£89.99
				Total amount

◄◄ Exercise 6 on page 310

E

Name	Boy/girl	Eye colour	Hair colour	Height
Carl	boy	blue	blonde	152cm
Sudi	girl	brown	black	160cm
Claire	girl	blue	brown	158cm
Huw	boy	brown	black	155cm
Rob	boy	green	blonde	152cm
Menna	girl	brown	black	157cm
Brenda	girl	blue	brown	158cm

1. What colour hair does Carl have?
2. How tall is Menna?
3. What colour eyes does Rob have?
4. Write down the names of people with brown eyes.
5. Write down the names of the girls with blue eyes.
6. Write down how tall the boy with brown eyes is.

Quick Test 8

A Write down the answers to these.

1.	36	2.	89	3.	57	4.	91
	+ 13		− 37		+ 39		− 68

B This table shows the number of wins.

1. How many wins did Team 3 have in the 2nd round?
2. How many wins did Team 4 have in the 1st round?
3. How many wins did Team 1 have altogether?
4. Which team had the most wins altogether?

Soccer Teams

	1st round	2nd round
Team 1	6	7
Team 2	5	4
Team 3	1	3
Team 4	0	2
Team 5	8	7

C
1. 51 players tried out for the school soccer teams.
They needed 24 players.
How many missed out?
2. 19 from Year 7 and 17 from Year 8 tried out.
How many is this altogether?

D
1. What position does Dean play?
2. How old is Gary?
3. What year is Ed in?
4. Write down the names of the Year 11 players.
5. Write down the names of the Year 10 players who are 14.
6. One of the Year 11 players is 16. What position does he play?

Name	Year	Age	Position
Luke	10	13	sweeper
Gary	11	15	right wing
Steve	9	13	right back
David	8	12	reserve
Dele	10	14	centre half
Dylan	11	15	left back
Ed	11	16	centre
Dean	7	11	goal keeper
Farid	10	15	striker
Tom	9	13	left wing
Owen	10	14	sweeper
Clive	11	15	striker